DRUG ADDICTS: ARE THEY OUT OF CONTROL?

DRUG ADDICTS: ARE THEY OUT OF CONTROL?

John C. Brady, II,. Ph.D.

WESTERN BOOK/JOURNAL PRESS

San Mateo, California

1990

Manufactured in the United States of America By:

Western Book/Journal Press
P. O. Box 5226
San Mateo, California 94402

ISBN: 0-936029-24-2
Library of Congress Catalog Number: 90-71961

Library of Congress Cataloging-in-Publication Data:
    Brady, John
    Drug Addicts: Are They Out of Control?

Cover design by Robert A. Anthony

To Obtain Additional Copies of this Book,
Write or Call:

    Psychology Systems, Inc.
    615 South Main Street
    Milpitas, CA   95035
    1-(800) 992-8448

LIST OF CONTENTS

ACKNOWLEDGMENTS

Many people have contributed to this study. A variety of colleagues have made valuable suggestions. First, I want to thank the cooperative CRC research sample, without which there may never have been DRUG ADDICTS: ARE THEY OUT OF CONTROL?

The professional staff at the California Rehabilitation Center helped set up the research design. Mr. George Sing in 1970, and Assistant Warden Robert Groves and Josie Coria in 1990, were the key CRC "brass" who helped this writer get state approval to conduct this project. Also, the writer cordially thanks Mr. Robert Dickover, Research Specialist at the California Department of Corrections in Sacramento, California, who also helped "cut the proverbial red tape" and get this project approved by the State of California.

I wish to also thank Nancy McFall, who tolerated what seemed to be an endless succession of rough drafts. Organization, another skill possessed by Nancy, greatly facilitated this project's sense of order and helped bring it to completion.

I would also like to thank Mr. Jim Valiton of COMPtech Systems for his expertise in manuscript layout, without which publication of this book would not have been possible.

FOREWORD

Twenty years ago the country faced a drug crisis, the magnitude of which had not been previously experienced in this century. In 1970 I was involved in chemical dependency research at the University of California at Berkeley. At that time I believed that the country would never again see the level of drug use evidenced during the late 1960's and early 1970's. I was mistaken! A 1990 drug research report, also conducted at the University of California, concludes that "drug abuse among young people is one of the greatest challenges of our time. Almost daily, we are besieged by media reports of drug-related tragedy"*.

In 1970 I conducted the first California Rehabilitation Center (CRC) study. In 1990 I returned to CRC in an attempt to duplicate the original study to determine if drug abuser measures of locus of control and self-concept had changed over the years.

The earlier study of CRC drug users' locus of control and self-concept was originally published by Mayor Joseph Alioto's San Francisco Criminal Justice Council in 1973. The research took place in early 1970. The mayor's office chose to publish this particular CRC study in order to encourage an exchange of views on chemical dependency treatment practices. It was felt that this study was particularly germane to the field of drug treatment in California because it was conducted at the California Rehabilitation Center, CRC, the State's largest correctional facility to treat civilly committed drug abusers. It is hoped that these combined results (both the 1970 and 1990) will be shared not only with professionals but also the average citizen who desires to better understand the dynamics of drug abuse, as well as innovative forms of treatment for drug users.

*SHEDLER, J. and BLOCK, J.   Adolescent Drug Use and Psychological Health - A Longitudinal Inquiry. Amer. Psychol., 5, 612.

DRUG ADDICTS ARE NOT AFFLICTED WITH A DISEASE

This book shows that drug addicts, rather than having a medical disease, are in fact out of control psychologically. In addition to being out of control, this study shows that a chief reason for using drugs is the user's poor self-concept formation, as well as feelings of being "out of control". The use of drugs in today's society is the single most important social, psychological and legal problem facing the nation. Very little of the millions of dollars spent to combat the drug war is currently spent on chemical dependency treatment.

Now this study of one of the country's largest drug rehabilitation centers attempts to answer important questions related to drug addiction and treatment:

- Why are drug addicts out of control?

- What happens to a drug addict's self-concept?

- Is social class related to drug use?

- What is the most effective type of treatment?

- What role does age have in repeat drug use?

- Can education help stop the American drug dilemma?

- Does ethnic background affect drug use?

- How can we increase the drug user's success rate?

- Does marijuana use lead to "hard drugs"?

ENDORSEMENTS

For the past seven years Dr. Brady has been conducting chemical dependency research projects. This updated study of the California Rehabilitation Center provides us with new and important psychological information about drug addiction. In my view, we need the quality research contained in DRUG ADDICTS: ARE THEY OUT OF CONTROL?, in order to begin to combat today's increasing chemical dependency problem. Unraveling the personality dynamics of the drug user seems to be a logical first step toward a more complete understanding of why people turn to drugs.

Dr. Harold Geist
author of fifteen books, practicing psychologist, Berkeley, California, distinguished member of Psychology Systems, Inc., Health Care Plan.

DRUG ADDICTS: ARE THEY OUT OF CONTROL? represents the other and positive side of the California Rehabilitation Center story. After having worked at this institution for over 20 years, and after reading so many unflattering accounts of what goes on at CRC, I can say that Dr. Brady's study depicts a different and more humane side of this institution. He took the time and made the effort to examine the psychological characteristics of the CRC residents. Dr. Brady's conclusions are useful and his study casts an important light on this state's drug abuse problem.

Robert Grove
Associate Warden The California Rehabilitation Center

During the past 15 years I have had a continuing interest in the treatment programs provided for those addicted to a variety of chemical substances. As Director of the Santa Clara County Drug Abuse Services, I noticed that meaningful follow-up research studies were conspicuously absent. DRUG ADDICTS: ARE THEY OUT OF CONTROL?, written by Dr. John C. Brady, II, provides us with valuable new information concerning the treatment of chemical dependency in one of the country's largest settings for rehabilitation. Dr. Brady's study provides us with definitive information concerning why drug users begin to abuse chemical substances. Furthermore, his findings strongly suggest that people select drugs in order to overcompensate for a low self-concept and because they have internal psychological feelings of being out of control.

Alan P. Brauer, M.D., Director
The Brauer Medical Center
Former Director, Santa Clara County Drug Abuse Services
Diplomate, American Board of Psychiatry & Neurology

INTRODUCTION

By JAMES NIELSEN, M.S.W.

President, CalNet

(California Network of Behavioral Health Services)

During the 1920's the California Rehabilitation Center, now one of the nation's largest institutions for drug rehabilitation, was built as a health spa catering to some of Hollywood's biggest motion picture stars. The "rich and famous" frequented the Norco resort to use the natural sulfur springs plentiful in the area. Later the State of California purchased the property and converted it to a correctional treatment facility.

Interestingly enough, only a few research projects have been conducted at this very important center. Dr. Brady's 1970 research on locus of control and self-concept with a drug abuse sample represents an important work which differentiates drug abusers on the basis of the psychodynamics; specifically on the locus of control and self-concept dimensions. It is also of interest to note that not one federal government or state dollar was contributed to subsidize either of Dr. Brady's studies, notwithstanding the fact that the federal government has a current budget of Fiscal Year 1990 totalling $7,864 billion!

This updated work -- Drug Addicts: Are they Out of Control? -- compares the earlier results with the 1990 results. During the past twenty years, Dr. Brady has remained a leading authority on drug treatment, as well as the costs associated with providing such treatment.

Even though there has been some success working with chemically dependent patients, chemical dependency still remains one of the nation's largest social problems. It is clear that the U. S. must begin to spend more time and money on chemical dependency treatment and less on attempts to see the problem as a legal or law enforcement issue. It seems fairly obvious that more arrests of drug users will not solve the problem. Unfortunately, the federal government is still consumed by the use of a control system stressing interdiction and arrest rather than a treatment system.

More than one million drug abusers are treated each year, yet there is precious little follow-up to determine why these people turned to drugs. Dr. Brady's study provides us with increased knowledge concerning why individuals turn to drugs initially and what they look like psychologically. It is of great import that this study, one of the few to my knowledge, is to examine the same psychological personality factors twenty years later.

Dr. Brady's use of locus of control and self-concept as personality factors provides in depth understanding of the drug user. Locus of control, or a person's perception of how much control or power they have over their lives, is important psychologically. Likewise, self-concept is an important explanatory variable.

Dr. Brady related this perception of power and self-concept measurements to youthful versus older users and first time users versus repeat offenders. This study goes a long way towards filling an important research gap. Additionally, because of these research conclusions, we are also in a better position to provide specific programs for certain types of drug users. It is my suggestion that we begin to fund projects such as Dr. Brady's instead of using additional monies to wage an almost "unwinable war" against the drug problem. It is my impression that if we do not begin to fund these types of research projects we may face an even larger U. S. drug crisis.

James Nielsen, M.S.W.

CHAPTER I

THE CURRENT DRUG PROBLEM

Is It Out of Control?

A Short History of Drugs in America

Drug use and abuse has reached epidemic proportions in this country. Drug abuse among young people is reported to be one of the greatest challenges of the 1990s (1). The use of heroin, once thought to be restricted to urban ghetto areas, has now diffused into all socioeconomic strata. Current heroin addicts are estimated at roughly half a million. A Senate subcommittee estimates that about 2.2 million Americans are "hard-core coke heads". California and New York are the leading states, each with more than 450,000 addicts. Drug addiction mounts appallingly among the American work force. The U. S. government estimates that 12% of the work force uses drugs. Now most companies, irrespective of corporate position, subject employees to a urine drug-detection test before hiring and routinely contract for an Employee Assistance Plan (EAP). Those individuals found to be on drugs are rejected for employment, or after employment they are referred to the company's EAP for treatment.

Furthermore, the National Institute on Drug Abuse estimates that twenty percent of today's school children use drugs experimentally. In addition to the widespread use of cocaine and its derivatives (crack) and other natural drugs, chemistry has produced an entirely new range of psychoactive agents, whose attendant dangers are only now being recognized. Chemistry has ushered in a host of new drugs labeled "designer drugs." "In a sense," says Dr. Mark Gold, founder of the 800-COCAINE Hotline, "Crack is an example of a designer drug, since its development resulted from experimentation by street chemists with cocaine powder" (2). Officials from the U. S. Office of National Drug Control Policy recently stated that four million Americans have a serious chemical dependency problem, defined as using any drug four or more times a week (3). It has been estimated that eighty percent of our heroin population is now white, and a big proportion of that eighty percent is middle class.

Presently it appears that the U. S. consumption of drugs is increasing. However, more young people realize that the use of illegal drugs, especially cocaine, is dangerous. In 1988 the National Institute on Drug Abuse released the results of a nationwide high school survey. Table 1 presents the results of this survey (4).

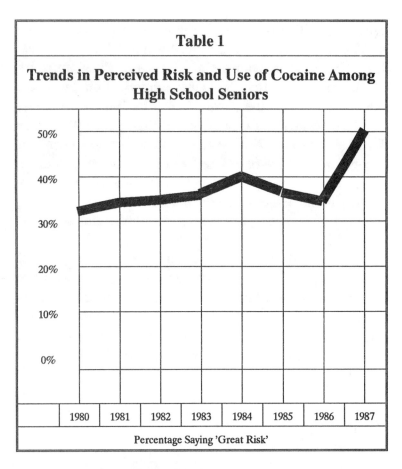

Table 1

Trends in Perceived Risk and Use of Cocaine Among High School Seniors

Percentage Saying 'Great Risk'

It is quite apparent the 1987 sample perceived cocaine to be more dangerous than did their 1980-86 cohorts. According to the 1989 PRIDE Survey (Parents' Resource Institute for Drug Education) of high school students, the nation's drug problem is only getting worse and not better! Dr. Gleaton, president of PRIDE, stated, "we have

4

little reason to rejoice over these findings (5)."   The
results of this important nationwide survey indicated:

- Only 22 percent of the Class of '89 was drug-free.
  The other 78 percent admitted using a drug or
  alcoholic beverage during the past year.

- Junior high drug use was actually up in cases.

- We detected weekly cocaine use in the sixth grade.

- Cigarette smoking soared in all grades.

- More dramatic was the trend for senior high
  marijuana users: use was down from 27% in '84-
  85 to 22% today, but the level of intoxication went
  up from 56% getting "very high" or "stoned" in
  '84-85, to 66% in '88-89.

- Fewer senior high students drank liquor, down
  from 54% to 52%, but again more of them reached
  higher levels of intoxication, up from 46% to 51%.

- Beer drinking by senior high students declined
  from 68% to 61% while intoxication levels stayed
  about the same.

- In junior high school, cocaine and liquor use rose over four years ago, and marijuana use dropped by less than 1%.

- More junior high students reported drinking liquor, an increase from 21% to 25% in four years, and more of them used cocaine, from 1.3% to 1.7%. (Cocaine and "crack" are a single drug category in the PRIDE Questionnaire).

- Progress was made at the junior high level in marijuana smoking, which dropped from 8.1% to 7.6% over 4 years, and in beer drinking, down from 40% to 38%.

- The percentage of junior high students reporting cigarette smoking in '88-89 jumped by 8% since '84-85, from 20% to 28%. Likewise, senior high students reported increased cigarette smoking, from 33% to 39%.

On an encouraging note, the survey also found fewer senior high school students (grades 9-12) consumed beer, liquor, marijuana and cocaine compared with four years ago.

Official drug policy has always been problematic. The principal objective of government programs is to reduce the number of addicts, and whether this drive for abstinence results in more or less crime appears to be of secondary concern. The attitude could be summarized as follows: pass legislation and enforce laws for programs that will get addicts off narcotics and keep them "clean," with the hope that this approach will result in reduced crime and less economic cost to the taxpayer.

But if this approach does not work, then just keep going ahead anyway, spending more of the public's money, passing tougher laws, and advocating stricter enforcement, regardless of the consequences. More than twenty years ago Governor Nelson A. Rockefeller of New York reflected this point of view in a speech on November 24, 1969, when he defended his state's drug program against criticism by contending, "They (the critics) are saying, in effect, that we have failed in thirty-six months to end a problem as old as man. The problem that we should focus on, however, is the damage inflicted on society by addicts; this does not go back to the beginning of man but only to the inception of our present public policy, which began in the 1920s (6)."

More recently even President Bush, in mid-February 1990, flew into the center of the South American drug exportation capital, Cartagena, Columbia, in order to flex the U.S.'s muscles and to escalate the military war against the powerful drug cartels. It is the government's view that saber rattling will be an effective way to deal with drug lords. Don't bet on it!

One method toward controlling this disturbing increase in drug abuse, traditionally the approach most resorted to, has been through increased governmental legal regulation. A law enforcement philosophy pervades such a legalistic approach. Both state and federal legislators have considered bills urging reformation of the laws controlling drug addiction and traffic. Many of these laws have proved punitive and retaliatory; they proffered long prison terms rather than attempting to come to terms with the issues of cause, effective control and treatment.

Especially, this appears to be the case among youthful marijuana consumers. Enforcement of stringent drug regulations may serve to worsen the problem by engendering a disrespect or apathy for not only the drug statutes but for the entire system of criminal justice in America.

The U.S. involves multiple federal agencies including the FBI, IRS, Customs Service, Drug Enforcement Agency (DEA), U. S. Coast Guard, Department of the Treasury, the U. S. Marines, the Office of National Drug Control Policy, the National Institute on Drug Abuse and the U. S. Army to combat illegal drug use. This bureaucratic tangle of agencies may further serve to confuse coping with the drug epidemic rather than solving it. One fact is clear - the government's position is primarily based on a law enforcement philosophy.

The government's law enforcement model of drug addiction and drug trafficking has been traditionally associated with both the criminal images of the addict and the criminal underworld surrounding drug dealers and marketplace. Therefore, the partial failure of the Drug Enforcement Agency, (DEA), can be seen as the enactment of self-fulfilling prophecy. This agency was charged with the responsibility of enforcing all laws regulating drug use and assigned the role of controlling the illegal manufacture and sale of all new synthetic drugs. Indeed, this was a formidable undertaking. Because of the difficult nature of the task and because of low salaries offered to employees, the agency is waging what seems to be an unwinable war against drugs. In a very persuasive study - the Rand Study - researchers have concluded that further governmental interdiction of narcotics traffickers would at best reduce U. S. cocaine consumption by only 5% (7).

Another method for curbing the drug problem rests with the rehabilitation of the drug addict. Prior to the 1980's many drug addicts who became involved with the law were referred to one of the two United States Public Health Service Hospitals (USPHSH). These facilities, once operated as hospitals, have now been converted to correctional settings. Until recently there was little in the way of drug treatment available at the state level. It is understood that these federal hospitals have failed in their efforts to appreciably reduce the recidivism rate among releasees. For instance, a relapse rate ranging up to ninety-four percent as reported in one follow-up investigation of a former USPHSH facility makes it urgent that we reassess the present legal controls and forms of institutional treatment for the drug addict (8).

According to U.S. Government sources drug treatment programs are quite diverse, reflecting variations in types and severity of drug use, and in strategies used to treat it. Most of the nation's 5,000 drug treatment programs fall under one of five broad categories: detoxification programs, usually inpatient, which have the short-range goal of ending users' physical addiction to drugs; chemical dependency units, mainly private inpatient or residential three-to four-week programs; outpatient clinics, which offer counseling and support for those who want to quit using drugs while they continue to function in the community; methadone maintenance programs, which treat heroin addicts by coupling counseling with the administration of methadone, a prescription medication that "blocks" the craving for heroin while eliminating the usual pain of withdrawal; and residential therapeutic communities, where users spend up to 18 months in a highly structured program to end their drug addiction. In addition, there are support groups such as

Narcotics Anonymous, which can be effective as either a substitute for or an extension of other approaches.

One reason for the failure of these programs under governmental sponsorship can be related to the tenacious policy of viewing the addict as a criminal and then applying criminal sanctions to his behavior and not implementing programs of psychotherapy. In most cases governmental rehabilitation centers have been operated as correctional institutions and the treatment there has involved little more than detoxification and custody.

Besides treatment of the drug addict as a criminal, another outstanding deficiency in traditional programs has been the almost total absence of adequate follow-up care and supervision after release. The drug addict is merely detoxified, then released back to the community free to engage in the same life style that perhaps fostered the addiction. An effective rehabilitation program must come to terms with the mental attitude of the addict during periods of hospital care and continued therapy after release.

Another approach for reducing the drug problem is through the development of more explanatory psychological theories of drug causation. If we are to reduce and effectively control the drug dilemma and provide adequate forms of treatment, it is important to identify and describe the personality dynamics of the drug user.

Investigations have attempted to unravel the personality configurations of drug users from the standpoint of a variety of theoretical perspectives. For instance, Fenichel's (9) historic psychoanalytical interpretation of drug use, set down more than forty-five years ago, still serves as a paradigm for contemporary analytical researchers. Besides psychoanalytical interpretations there are other theoretical frameworks from which to understand drug use. MacDonald (10) has developed a social-environmental theory which quantifies certain personality features of the drug abuser not treated by the psychoanalytical models. The theories of drug causation do cast some light on the personality of the drug addict, yet there have been few empirical investigations designed to differentiate among drug addicts. Accurate differentiation can lead to differential treatment programs for drug-dependent individuals; instead of assuming that one type of treatment will effectively serve all addicts.

Long term studies concerning the psychological reasons for drug abuse have been sparse. One exception is a 1990 investigation done by psychologists at the University of California, Berkeley, that strongly support the notion that there are important psychological antecedents for drug abuse (11). These researchers conclude that frequent drug users appeared to be relatively maladjusted as children. Frequent users were characterized as having problems with moral issues, stress, no future orientation, low self-confidence, low self-concept, feeling unworthy and feeling controlled by others; victims or feeling they cannot control their lives.

The researchers relate:

> Drug abuse among young people is one of the greatest challenges of our time. Almost daily, we are besieged by media reports of drug-related tragedy, of shootings in our schools, gang warfare, and overdose-related deaths. As an increasing share of society's resources is diverted toward coping with the drug problem and its consequences, the need for sound, scientific information on the factors contributing to drug use is urgent (12).

In this important study the researchers examined:

> The relation between psychological characteristics and drug use was investigated in subjects studied longitudinally, from preschool through age 18. Adolescents who had engaged in some drug experimentation (primarily with marijuana) were the best-adjusted in the sample. Adolescents who used drugs frequently were maladjusted, showing a distinct personality

syndrome marked by interpersonal alienation, poor impulse control, and manifest emotional distress. Adolescents who, by age 18, had never experimented with any drug were relatively anxious, emotionally constricted and lacking in social skills.

Psychological differences between frequent drug users, experimenters, and abstainers could be traced to the earliest years of childhood and related to the quality of parenting received. The findings indicate that (a) problem drug use is a symptom, not a cause, of personal and social maladjustment, and (b) the meaning of drug use can be understood only in the context of an individual's personality structure and developmental history. It is suggested that current efforts at drug prevention are misguided to the extent that they focus on symptoms rather than on the psychological syndrome underlying drug abuse (13).

Certain non-psychiatric physicians think of the drug user as:

An immature, weak, hedonistic, and rebellious individual. He is inordinately sensitive to bodily discomfort, unable to establish long-range goals, incapable of meeting the demands of his environment, and frequently hostile to society. However, at the present time we do not have adequate psychiatric knowledge to treat these character disorders, at least in the majority of cases. We do not even have adequate evidence that the addict differs from members of his society who face the same, often hostile, environment, without turning to drugs. There is no well-defined addict personality type which would fit into established psychiatric categories. We do know that the relapse rate is high, particularly among the younger addicts, and that the most frequent complications of their habitual drug use are sociological. It has therefore been clear up to now that no definite prescribed method of successful treatment has been developed. The majority of physicians do not understand what therapy they can undertake with addicts and are frequently deterred by fears or misunderstandings of the present laws (14).

Hopefully, this study will provide psychological information helpful in both the classification and treatment of the drug user. A great deal of interest and concern for research regarding the addiction to drugs has been prevalent, but the drug abuser himself/herself has been neglected. There has been some progress made as far as the medical, psychological and social aspects of narcotics addiction is concerned, but the genesis of drug abuse and treatment of the abuser is still open to speculation. A host of questions must be answered before the battle against narcotics addition can be successfully waged (15).

Moreover, drug addiction research has not dealt with the problem of recidivism; the return to the use of drugs, perhaps the least understood aspect involved in chemical dependency pathology. Further complicating the recidivism issue is the role played by such variables as the drug user's age, educational level and ethnic background. The study of the differences between age and ethnic background for drug users has for the most part gone unnoticed and unresearched.

THE PRESENT STUDY

This present study (including the 1970 study) used locus of control and self-concept variables, important psychological dimensions in order to differentiate between a group of institutionalized first and recidivist drug offenders who are divided by age and ethnicity committed to the California Rehabilitation Center, CRC. CRC is one of the largest drug treatment facilities in the country. A full description of CRC is presented in Chapter II. The locus of control and self-concept dimensions not previously assessed between these two groups of drug users were chosen for their proven value with other deviant groups such as prisoners, alcoholics and sex offenders.

The internal-external locus of control dimension, or simply "locus of control", was the first psychological variable used in this CRC study. This dimension reflects the degree to which an individual tends to feel that the rewards for his actions or behavior are determined by his own acts (internal locus of control or simply internality) or are dependent upon forces outside of himself (external locus of control or simply externality).

Previous investigations have demonstrated that certain deviant groups such as federal prisoners [16], female juvenile delinquents [17] and neurotics [18] reflect an external locus of control. In keeping with these studies it follows that drug users who depend upon an outside or exterior reward system to run their lives would also show high externality, i.e., belief that they are being controlled. It is the writer's assumption that drug users rely primarily upon externality, thus feeling their lives are controlled [19].

The second variable under investigation in this study was self-concept. Rogers'[20] definition of self-concept was utilized throughout this research: "The self-concept or self-structure may be thought of as an organized configuration of perceptions of the self which are admissible to awareness. It is composed of such elements as the perceptions of one's characteristics and abilities."

This personality dimension has been accepted as an important construct in psychology for the past seventy-five years and there is evidence to establish a relationship between the type of self-concept a person exhibits and the possible range of behavior in which he will engage. More importantly, investigators have found that certain deviant groups such as alcoholics, (21) mental patients, (22) sex offenders, (23) and criminals (24) manifest similarly unfavorable self-concepts. In this study it was hypothesized that drug users, like other deviants, would present unfavorable self-concepts.

Accepting the premise that both locus of control and self-concept are important personality variables bound-up with drug addiction, and that systematic investigation of the drug user's personality has the potential to bring the causes of drug use into sharper focus, the main purpose of this study was to determine the differences of measures of locus of control and self-concept between first and recidivist drug offenders as separated by age and ethnicity. In addition, the relationships of social economic status was related to locus of control and self-concept measures.

On the premise that locus of control and self-concept are interdependent personality constructs, a third goal was to determine the relation between internality and favorable self-concept.

There have been a number of investigations of both the locus of control dimensions and self-concept among a wide variety of deviant populations in the field of criminology. Yet, such studies with drug users have been conspicuously absent from the literature.

CRC Patient/Inmate Sample

Initially this investigation (1970) used two matched samples of resident drug users at the California Rehabilitation Center, CRC (25). The second sample (1990) was also comprised of two matched samples. One sample was composed of twenty-four first drug offenders and the other of an equivalent number of recidivist drug offenders. The groups were divided into two equal age groups: youth offenders (18 to 26 years) and older offenders (27 to 35 years), and were further subdivided into three equal ethnic groups: Blacks, Mexican-Americans and Whites. All subjects were chosen on the basis of simple random sampling procedure from the larger population at the California Rehabilitation Center.

Prior to the date of testing the investigator devised a subject selection procedure (Tables 1,2) in order to obtain two equally sized matched samples (N = 24) of first and recidivist offenders. Table 1 presents the 1970 research sample and Table 2 presents the 1990 research sample. Both samples comprised forty-eight drug offenders. On the suggestion of the CRC administration, the sample size for this investigation consisted of less than 100 residents. The investigator presented the experimental design to the CRC research staff, and the 48 subjects were randomly chosen from the larger population until each cell in the research design was filled. All subjects had resided in CRC at least six weeks prior to the testing; thus minimizing the effects of "commitment shock," which holds that the fact of recent arrest and incarceration would tend to depress the inmate and invalidate the results of psychological testing.

Table 1				
CRC Research Sample Subdivided by Offender Drug Status, Age and Ethnicity, 1970 Sample				
		First Drug Offenders		Recidivist Offenders	
		N = 24		N = 24	
		Younger N = 12	Older N = 12	Younger N = 12	Older N = 12
White	N = 16	N = 4	N = 4	N = 4	N = 4
Mex-Amer.	N = 16	N = 4	N = 4	N = 4	N = 4
Black	N = 16	N = 4	N = 4	N = 4	N = 4

Table 2				
CRC Research Sample Subdivided by Offender Drug Status, Age and Ethnicity, 1990 Sample				
		First Drug Offenders		Recidivist Offenders	
		N=24		N=24	
		Younger N=12	Older N=12	Younger N=12	Older N=12
White N=16		N=4	N=4	N=4	N=4
Mex-Amer. N=16		N=4	N=4	N=4	N=4
Black N=16		N=4	N=4	N=4	N=4

Thus, two equal samples (N=24) of first and recidivist offenders, were formed. These groups were then bifurcated on the basis of age into two groups, younger residents (18-26 years) and older residents (27-35 years). Furthermore, each of these samples were matched with respect to ethnicity. Three equal sized ethnic groups (N = 16) were formed: Whites, Mexican-Americans and Blacks. (See Tables 1, 2). While ethnicity was not included as a specific research variable, the data from a comparison of these ethnic groups were reported because of future implications ethnic background might play on locus of control and self-concept studies.

PSYCHOLOGICAL TERMS USED IN THIS INVESTIGATION

1. <u>Locus of Control</u>. The term locus of control and internal-external control are used interchangeably throughout this investigation, although the writer tended to favor the term locus of control.

Rotter succinctly defined locus of control in the following way:

When a reinforcement is perceived by the subject as following some action of his own but not being entirely contingent upon his action, then, in our culture, it is typically perceived as the result of luck, chance, fate, as under the control of powerful others, or an unpredictable because of the great complexity of the forces surrounding him. When the event is interpreted in this way by an individual, we have labeled this a belief in external control. If the person perceives that the event is contingent upon his own behavior or his own relatively permanent characteristics, we have termed this a belief in internal control (26).

2. <u>Self-Concept</u>. The terms self and self-concept as used in this investigation closely followed Rogers' definitions.

These terms refer to the organized, consistent conceptual gestalt composed of perceptions of the characteristics of the "I" or "me" to others and to various aspects of life, together with the values attached to these perceptions. It is a gestalt which is available to awareness though not necessarily in awareness (27).

In other words, while the internal person believes that reinforcements are contingent upon his own behavior, the external person believes that reinforcements are determined by forces independent of his own behavior. Stated in another way, the internal person has been characterized as seeking autonomy, independence, will take reasonable risk, has positive self-confidence and perceived control over situations (28).

3. Socio-economic Status. One of the most representative measures of socio-economic status is derived from a consideration of four status characteristics: occupation, source of income, house type, and general residential area. Warner stated that economic and other prestige factors are highly important and closely correlated with social class; and that these social and economic factors, such as talent, income, and money, if their potentialities for rank are to be realized, must be translated into social-class behavior acceptable to members of any given social level of the community (29).

CHAPTER I

REFERENCES

1. SHEDLER, J. and BLOCK, J. "Adolescent Drug Use and Psychological Health - A Longitudinal Inquiry". *Amer. Psychol.*, 5, p. 612.

2. GOLD, M. *The facts about drugs and alcohol.* New York: Bantam Books, 1988, p. 114.

3. BIDEN, J. *Senate Julian Committee on Drugs,* 5-1990.

4. NATIONAL DRUG CONTROL STRATEGY, U. S. Government Printing Office, p. 54.

5. PRIDE, "Class of '89 only 22% Drug-Free", *PRIDE*, 1989.

6. STRAUS, N. *Addicts and Drug Abusers*, Twayne Press, 1971, pp.14-15.

7. REUTER, P. *Rand Corporation Narcotics Abuse Study*, June 1989.

8. DUVALL, H. J., LOCK, B. Z. and BRILL, L. "Follow-up study of narcotic drug addicts five years after hospitalization.", *Public Health Rep.*, 1963, 78, pp.185-193.

9. FENICHEL, OTTO. *Psychoanalytic theory of the neurosis.* New York: Norton, 1950.

10. MACDONALD, L. "Narcotic addition: A new point of view". In Harms, E. (ed.). *Drug addition in youth.* Oxford: Pergamon Press, 1965.

11. SHEDLER, J. and BLOCK, J. "Adolescent Drug Use and Psychological Health - A Longitudinal Inquiry". *Amer. Psychol.*, 5, p. 612.

12. SHEDLER, J. and BLOCK, J. "Adolescent Drug Use and Psychological Health - A Longitudinal Inquiry". *Amer. Psychol.*, 5, p. 612.

13. SHEDLER, J. and BLOCK, J. "Adolescent Drug Use and Psychological Health - A Longitudinal Inquiry". *Amer. Psychol.*, 5, p. 612.

14. GREENBERG, S.G. "The View of a Practicing Physician", in STRAUS, N. *Addicts and Drug Abusers.* New York: Twayne, 1971, p. 56.

15. ALL ABOUT THE CIVIL ADDICT PROGRAM, State of California, 2-1988.

16. LADWIG, G. W. Personal, situational and social determinants of preference for delayed reinforcement. Un-

published doctoral dissertation, Ohio State University, 1963.

17 FITTS, W. H. and HAMNER, W. T. "The self concept and delinquency: studies on the self concept and rehabilitation". Nashville mental health center Monogr., 1969, 1, pp. 1-96.

18. FEATHER, N. T. "Some personality correlates of external control". *Australian J. Psychol.*, 1967, 19, pp. 253-260.

19. BRADY, J. C. "Psychological Dimensions of drug abuse". City San Francisco; Criminal Justice Publication, 1972.

20. ROGERS, C. R. *Client Centered Therapy.* Cambridge Riverside Press. 1951. p. 136.

21. WAHL, C. W. "Some antecedent factors in the family histories of 109 alcoholics". *Quart. J. Stud. Alcohol.*, 1956, 17, pp. 643-654.

22. KOGAN, W. S., QUINN, R. Ax. A. F. and RIPLEY, H. S. "Some methodological problems in the quantification of Clinical assessment" by Q array. *J. consult. Psychol.*, 1957, 21, pp. 57-72.

23. HURLEY, W. H. A study of the self-concepts of criminals and non-criminals. Unpublished doctoral dissertation. The University of Oklahoma, 1961.

24. COHEN, B. J. and VENER, A. M. "Self-concept modification and total correctional institutions". *J. correctional Ed.*, 1968, 20, pp. 8-15.

25. CALIFORNIA REHABILITATION CENTER, Survey Conducted in 1970.

26. ROTTER, J. B. "Generalized expectancies for internal versus external control of reinforcement". *Psychol. Monogr.*, 1966, 80, p.I-27.

27. KOCH, S. (ed.), *Psychology: a study of a science* (Vol. 3), New York: McGraw-Hill, 1959.

28. STICKLAND, B. Internal-external control expectancies. *Amer. Psychol.* 1989, 44, pp. 1-7.

29. WARNER, W. L, MEEKER, M. L. and EELLS, K. W. *Social class in America.* New York:Harper Torchbooks, 1960.

CHAPTER II

RESEARCH SETTING

CALIFORNIA REHABILITATION CENTER

Once a Health Spa For the Rich and Famous

The California Rehabilitation Center, CRC, which has been of interest to the writer for more than 20 years, was an ideal setting to complete both locus of control and self-concept studies. The writer's first study was conducted at CRC in June 1970. A full 20 years have elapsed between the initial study and the present one.

Interestingly enough, CRC in Norco, California, was originally (c. 1920s) the site of an elaborate health spa nestled in the secluded San Bernardino mountain foothills 35 miles east of Los Angeles. The spa idea emerged when artesian wells were drilled and the water was heated. The water had a high sulfuric content widely believed to have a therapeutic effect.

In September, 1941, President Roosevelt commissioned the land for the U.S. Navy as a hospital. It was widely rumored that the president anticipated visiting the Norco facility during his trips to California. Mr. Roosevelt may have envisioned a restorative spa similar to his Warms Springs, Georgia retreat where he died in 1945. The original CRC was a home away from home for Hollywood's elite, including Bob Hope and others. Years later, when CRC became a drug rehabilitation center, a number of the children of the Hollywood stars sought care at the former health spa. The literature disseminated by CRC is replete with photos taken at the time the Norco facility was a quiet place for the "rich and famous."

CRC, throughout its history, has not always enjoyed favorable criticism from professionals. For example, one New York State Supreme Court judge, after visiting CRC, had these comments:

> There was one major "therapeutic center" for the entire State of California. It is a large, fortress-like building, in function a hospital, but in another sense a maximum-security prison. I remember returning one evening, because I slept there for several nights. Just before I approached the gate I heard shots ring out in the dark. After I entered I inquired as to what had been going on and was told that one of the patients had been trying to go over the walls. I never learned from that day until this whether the shots hit anyone, but obviously this was not quite a hospital setting. The treatment in California consisted of so-called--and I say so-called advisedly--group therapy. The patients who were there by compulsion, most of them under a sentence of up to seven years, were segregated into groups of thirty. They had a leader who was a manifest-ly unqualified group therapist. In the main,

his qualifications were a college degree, no particular social background, and he conducted the therapy session more or less as he saw fit. What we beheld in a couple of sessions would make one's hair stand on end.

From an objective standpoint at least, the use of narcotics may well be a violation of moral law. In addition, since addiction is to a greater or lesser degree contagious, the use of narcotics has an impact upon the common good of society. But experience plainly shows that the attempt to legislate addiction out of existence is generally futile. The enforcement programs, apart from their vast cost, have done much to sustain organized crime and to create occasions for the corrupt of enforcement offenders. Our present policy, in any practical sense, has been an unmitigated failure and a source of unnecessary cruelty (1).

Duster, a professor of sociology at the University of California at Berkeley, has viewed CRC strictly as a prison setting:

Despite its title and selected euphemisms about its operations, CRC is a prison in almost every sense of the word. Well over 90 percent of the inmates were brought in after a conviction, involuntarily. As in every prison, the custodial functions take precedence over every other function. The larger society, at all critical points, demands this.

Whenever there is an escape, the public's reaction insures that the custodial wing of a prison gets tighter control and more power, while those primarily concerned with treatment must bend and accommodate. The therapeutic part of the program, which is an explicitly stated reason-for-being of the institution, is dramatically curtailed by the very context of the institutional setting (2).

CRC has been in operation as a correctional drug treatment facility since 1961. By law CRC is to provide specific control and treatment for the civilly committed drug abusers. The Legislature, in 1961, enacted the original law establishing the California Civil Addict Program providing for the commitment and treatment of narcotic addicts and persons, who by repeated use of narcotics, were an imminent danger of becoming addicted. The law provided for the receiving, control, confinement, education, treatment and rehabilitation of such persons under the custody and administrative direction of the Department of Corrections (3).

In July of 1990, at the time of the second study, the total population of CRC equaled 4,750, with 2,088 male drug users and 2,662 felon inmates. Only several other investigators have turned their attention to the study of CRC. Duster also characterized CRC as worthy of research:

> Strategic for study not only because it is the first large institution of its kind, but also because it has served and will serve as a model for other states with a narcotics problem. At the present, New Jersey has already followed the model of CRC; and Illinois is looking over the program with careful interest. Ideally, the plan is to separate the addict population from other criminals locked up in prisons, and to administer a separate kind of therapeutic treatment designed particularly for the addict (4).

In 1963, as a result of several Supreme Court decisions, an extensive reorganization of the California civil commitment statute was undertaken. The Legislature amended sections of the law to place emphasis upon the treatment and prevention of and the protection of the public through control of those who were uncooperative or unresponsive. In a further effort the responsibility for administering the release (parole) program was transferred from the Adult Authority to the newly established

Narcotic Addict Evaluation Authority. In 1965, the Legislature placed the authority for the Civil Addict Program and the Narcotic Addict Evaluation Authority within the Welfare and Institutions Code.

The California Legislature further amended the Welfare and Institutions Code, as recently as 1980, changing the indeterminate seven-year commitment to a determinate sentence commensurate with the determinate sentencing act. In addition, at the discretion of the criminal court, the law provided for a period of parole under the jurisdiction of the Board of Prison Terms following the expiration of the civil commitment. On September 17, 1981, because of the unique problems associated with narcotic addiction, the Legislature again amended the Welfare and Institutions Code which requires the civil addict commitment to be released on parole under the jurisdiction of the Narcotic Addiction Evaluation Authority at the end of the confinement period (2/3 of the sentence) or expiration of sentence, whichever occurs first.

What Happens After Sentencing

Beginning when a person is sentenced, the CRC staff commences the rehabilitation process. During the first week the entering patient is given a complete physical examination and a battery of educational and vocational tests. Interviews are conducted and tentative curriculum plans are made for programs specifically tailored for each person's needs. These programs include vocational and academic education, self-help groups and work assignments to mention a few. This program is unusual in that it combines compulsory treatment in its Rehabilitation Center with voluntary enrollment in its outpatient program.

Several of the therapeutic-counseling features at CRC are: The psychologists and counselors who work with the residents on a continuing basis are the same individuals who provided the initial diagnosis. The variety of tests which are administered include: I.Q., Educational Achievement, Vocational Aptitude, and personality tests. A compilation is made of the residents' social and criminal history. In addition, a continuous effort is made to provide a program for non-felon addicts by a trained staff for both inpatients and outpatients; so that sufficient control is exercised in order to avoid damage either to the individual or to society, while leaving an opportunity for growth of the individual. Community or group living is emphasized within the institution, and as many staff as possible are made a part of the community (5).

Subsequent to release, the person is placed on outpatient status or civil parole. The parole program not only provides for strict supervision and control but mandatory anti-narcotic urine testing as well. Those tests allow for early detection of narcotic use. The program also provides for immediate intervention and prompt return to confinement of individuals who revert to narcotics use. Violators may turn themselves into the CRC for a limited placement (60 days or less). Many repeaters take advantage of this provision rather than becoming strung out on narcotics again and committing crimes in order to support their habits.

Once the civil addict reaches the expiration of the CRC commitment, the law provides for an extended period of parole up to 3 years. Individual drug users must be discharged upon reaching the expiration of commitment. If a person remains drug free and complies with the conditions of parole for one year, he/she may receive an early discharge and will be referred back to the committing county court for vacation of the civil commitment. In addition, a person may avoid parole supervision if he/she successfully completes the outpatient phase of the program prior to reaching the expiration of the civil commitment. Wood summarizes the California program as follows:

1. Getting the addict away from other citizens is not only good for the addict, but it also has two advantages: It reduces the danger of afflicting others with the same malady and it naturally diminished the peddler's market.

2. Once the addict is institutionalized, he may receive proper care and treatment.

3. After release, close supervision and regular testing for drug use provides an excellent method for controlling the addict.

4. If the addict is not adjusting properly to society and the rest of the community, this can be detected and he is returned to the Center.

5. These methods tend to protect society from the anti-social acts of the addict (6).

The following information concerns the CRC classification and vocational-educational programs available to addict residents (7).

Initial Classification System

1. The functions of Initial Classification at CRC are to:

A. Evaluate the needs and possible adjustment of the addict by discussing his/her program needs and possible program, advising the person of treatment/program resources and evaluating reactions; taking into account suitability for the Civil Addict Program.

B. Initiate an educational, vocational or work program, depending on the evaluation and needs of the individual and institution and set defined expectations.

C. Refer complex cases, i.e., those with suitability concerns, or dual jurisdiction cases to the Institution Classification Committee.

D. Recommend transfer of inappropriately placed cases at CRC, i.e., severe psychiatric cases.

E. Review and designate appropriate degree of custody or refer to Institution Classification where appropriate.

2. The purpose of Initial Classification in outlining a program and expectations for new residents should be with the eventual goal of preparing an individual for Outpatient Status. Therefore, Initial Classification will, with recommendation from the Correctional Counselor, take the following into account:

A. Address the person's educational, vocational or work program needs, and outline the program goals and expectations.

B. Determine suitability and program needs based on the extent of alcohol/drug usage and criminality.

C. The program outline should be designed to help the person develop self control and perhaps enhance self-concept and locus of control perceptions.

D. Determine psychiatric or psychological needs and refer to psychiatric services, if appropriate.

E. Designate involvement in specific Self-Help, cultural or other institutionally approved groups that would assist the person with his/her drug problem.

F. If appropriate, address person's behavioral problems that need correcting and outline specific behavioral expectations for the individual to achieve.

G. Consider any outstanding or possible holds, detainers or wants in relation to suitability.

H. Consider any medical concerns that would prevent the person from programming at CRC or participating in opportunities for Outpatient Status/parole.

3. The process and time frames at CRC are as follows:

A. Intake Process:

1. The person will be processed per CRC procedures.

2. The person will be assigned to the orientation dorm immediately.

B. Orientation Dorm (first seven days to thirty-five days):

1. Oriented to Director of Corrections and CRC rules and regulations and the N-number program (narcotic user).

2. Narcotic resident reception processing.

3. Bed moves to general population.

C. Narcotic Resident Reception:

1. Narcotic Resident Reception will:

a. Refer all new arrival Narcotic Residents to the respective reception unit offices for interview within seven to twenty-one days of arrival at CRC.

b. Complete Goals and Expectations during the interview, with a copy to the inmate and original to the Central file.

c. Gather information for the initial study and case summary during the interview. Central file will be reviewed for verification for information when available. The initial study and case summary will be dictated within forty-five days arrival and processed through the correctional counselor II to the unit typist for completion.

d. Complete the Narcotic Resident reception checklist to provide notification of completed case work and/or additional case concerns to unit staff. Copies of the checklist will be placed in the central file and one forwarded to the unit correctional counselor I via the correctional counselor II. The original will be retained in the Narcotic Resident reception office. The checklist will be forwarded to the correctional counselor II within twenty-one days of arrival to assist in timely scheduling of Narcotic Residents for initial evaluation by Unit Correctional Counselor by twenty-eight days from date of arrival.

    e. Request psychiatric referrals, arresting officer's report, and initial field studies when obvious needs exist.

D. CRC Records Office will begin to gather central file material immediately and complete central file within thirty days of reception at CRC, which will include:

1. Court Abstract Material.

2. Court appointed doctor's evaluation and recommendation.

3. Probation Officer's Report.

4. Legal summary sheets (completed at CRC).

5. Request Counselor II information and place in file and conduct existing records procedure.

6. FBI rap sheet.

7. A felon file request if individual is a dual commitment.

8. After file is completed, forward all Narcotic Residents files to reception correctional

counselor I automatically, for their review. New commitment files should be sent within ten to fourteen days of arrival as soon as files are made up. Returnee files should be sent immediately upon arrival of the file at CRC from the Region offices.

E. Unit Correctional Counselor reviews individual's Central file and interviews person as soon as possible after completion of Central file, not to exceed twenty-eight days, whether or not file is complete.

1. Correctional Counselor initiates requests when needed for:

   a. Arresting Officer's Report.

   b. Initial field study.

   c. Immigration and naturalization service interview.

   d. Psychiatric referral.

   e. Obtaining dual commitment central file from Records.

2. Correctional Counselor I determines any exclusion concerns to present to Initial Classification.

3.Correctional Counselor I completes Initial Classification worksheet with above items outlined prior to Initial Classification.

4. The Unit correctional counselor II is responsible to ensure proper scheduling of personal appearances before Initial Unit Classification Committee approximately twenty-eight days from date of arrival at CRC.

The following information concerns the total vocational-educational and work programs available at CRC.

Even with limited resources, CRC provides training in at least nineteen different vocational-trade programs. Table 1 lists these areas. Table 2 shows the academic programs available at CRC.

Table 1					
VOCATIONAL TRADE PROGRAMS AVAILABLE AT CALIFORNIA REHABILITATION CENTER					
	Availability			Course Length	Waiting Time
CRC Course	1/2 Day	Full Day	Min GPL	Months	Months
Air Conditioning**	No	Yes	8.5	5-6	2
Auto Technology**	No	Yes	7.5	16	2
Baking	No	Yes	6.0	6	2
Building Maint/ Minor Repair	No	Yes	8.5	6	2
Building Maint/ Minor Repair*	No	Yes	8.5	6	2
Drafting	No	Yes	8.5	6	2
Drafting*	No	Yes	8.5	6	3
Dry Cleaning**	No	Yes	6.5	9	2
Electronics-Digital	No	Yes	8.5	6	2
Electronics- TV Repair	No	Yes	8.5	6	2
Food Preparation	No	Yes	4.0	5	1
Food Preparation*	No	Yes	4.0	5	1
Janitorial Services	No	Yes	6.0	10	2
Janitorial Services*	No	Yes	6.0	10	2

Table 1 *Cont*					
VOCATIONAL TRADE PROGRAMS					
Meatcutting	No	Yes	7.0	8	2
Offset Printing	No	Yes	8.0	6	3
Painting	No	Yes	7.5	6	2
Silk Screening	No	Yes	8.0	6	2
Typewriter Repair**	No	Yes	8.5	8	2
Upholstery**	No	Yes	7.5	7	2
Word Processing Secretarial*	No	Yes	8.0	6	2
Word Processing Clerical*	No	Yes	4.0	6	2
* Women Only ** Co-Educational All Others - Men Only					

EDUCATION PROGRAM AVAILABLE AT CALIFORNIA REHABILITATION CENTER

GOAL: To provide information for individuals committed to Civil Addict Program to use in solving real problems both in the institution and in the community.

EMPHASIS: A positive institutional experience as a foundation for successful living in the community.

ACTIVITIES: Physical fitness
Contemporary health issues
Achieving your potential
Family portrait series
Job series
Job seeking series
Role of the NAEA Board
Conditions of Release\Parole
Role of the Parole Agent
Evaluation

LENGTH OF COURSE: 120 hours

TOTAL ENROLLMENT: 72 Male inmates; 24 Female inmates

STAFFING: Four Civil Service teachers, (three for men, one for woman), Inmate Aides (six for men, two for women).

EVALUATION: TABE
Staff Curriculum (Individual Competency and Knowledge)

TRACKING AND RECORDKEEPING INFORMATION: Participant's test data, program information and progress, attendance record, disciplinary data, and program evaluation.

48

CRC EDUCATION PROGRAM CURRICULUM

PHYSIOLOGY & DRUG LECTURE

History and Culture of Drugs and Alcohol Use
Circulatory System
Respiratory System
Brain and Central Nervous
Opiates
C.N.S. Depressants, Including Alcohol
Cocaine
Amphetamines and Other Stimulants
PCP, Marijuana
Nutrition and Addiction
Genetic Factors of Addiction
Disease Concept of Addiction
Progression of Addiction
Sexually Transmitted Diseases

SOCIAL-PSYCH LECTURES

Mental Health
Life Planning Perspectives
Stress
Perception
Attitudes and Habits
Aging and Facing Death
Self-Image and Building Self-Esteem
Sexuality
Relationships
Intervention
Communication
Responsibility
Success Principles
Goal Setting
Motivation
Finding a Job
Outside Agencies: How to find help
Expectations of NAEA Board
Program Requirements of N#
Domestic Violence and Child Abuse Prevention
Family Systems - Functional and Dysfunctional
Roles of Family Members - Families in Crisis
Criminal Behavior Patterns

Table 2					
ACADEMIC PROGRAMS **AVAILABLE AT CRC** **Men's Unit**					
	Availability				Average Waiting Time
Course	Part-Time	1/2 Day	Full Day	Evening	Corres.	(Months)
Adult Level I	No	No	Yes	Yes	No	0
Adult Level II	No	No	Yes	Yes	No	0
Business Education	No	No	Yes	No	No	0-1
ESL Lab	No	No	Yes	Yes	No	1-2
GED	No	No	Yes	No	No	0
High Interest Courses (Music)	No	Yes	Yes	No	No	0-1
College	Yes	Yes	No	Yes	Yes	0-1
Civil Commitment - Education Program	No	No	Yes	No	No	0

Table 3					
ACADEMIC PROGRAMS AVAILABLE AT CRC					
Women's Unit					
	Availability					Average Waiting Time
Course	Part-Time	1/2 Day	Full Day	Evening	Corres.	(Months)
Learning Lab	No	No	Yes	Yes	No	0
GED	No	No	Yes	No	No	0-1
College	Yes	No	No	Yes	Yes*	0-1
Civil Commitment - Education Program	No	No	Yes	No	No	0
*Correspondence courses must be paid for by the inmates.						
GED testing is usually done once a month.						

WORK PROGRAMS AVAILABLE AT CRC

(a) Maintenance - Not a training program; individuals must be skilled in one of the following trades:

(1) Carpentry

(2) **Plumbing**

(3) **Painting**

(4) **Electrician**

(5) **Mechanic Auto Shop**

(6) **Sheet Metal**

(7) **Refrigeration**

(8) **Welding**

(9) **Boiler Room/Power House**

(10) **Fire House/Structural**

(b) **Correctional Industries - (Men's and Women's Unit) - not a training program; unskilled or semi-skilled can be used if they are interested. Basic mass production piece work operation of a garment I industry.**

(1) **Sewing Machine Operators.**

(2) **Sewing Machine Mechanic (skilled).**

(3) **Garment Cutter (skilled).**

(c) **Support services and other institutional assignments.**

(1) Main Kitchen Workers.

(2) Warehouse Workers.

(3) Ground Maintenance/outside perimeter.

(4) Medical and Dental attendants.

(5) Typewriter/TV Repairmen.

(6) Porters all areas.

(7) Clerks all areas.

(8) Personnel services.

(9) Institutional Transportation (taxi).

(10) Yard crews/inside perimeter.

Forestry "Norco Camp #34"

(a) Must meet qualifying criteria.

(b) Sixty man camp of three crews of sixteen men each and twelve to twenty men on training.

THERAPEUTIC INVOLVEMENT AT CRC

(a) Correctional Counselors - counselors are encouraged to try a variety of group counseling approaches.

(b) Psychiatric Staff - individual and group psychotherapy for those who seek it or are required by or counseling staff.

(c) Religious programs.

>   (1) Full-time Catholic and Protestant chaplains; part-time Rabbi and Muslim chaplains (5).
>
>   (2) Approximately fifty different community organizations offer denominational services each week.
>
>   (3) Personal counseling and pastoral care.

Self-Development Opportunities

(a) Self-help groups:

>   (1) Alcoholics Anonymous
>
>   (2) Narcotics Anonymous
>
>   (3) American Indian Culture Group.
>
>   (4) Espejo-Prison Preventers.

(b) Pre-release - is a voluntary participation program which provides community resources, workshops, three week course and reentry opportunities to any inmate housed at the California Rehabilitation Center.

(1) Involvement with outside community groups: Volunteers of America, college groups, National Alliance of Business Workers Employment Resource Council of Orange County, Project Freedom, other groups.

(2) Direct services: D.M.V. (license-ID), E.D.D. (Los Angeles), D.V.R. (San Diego), Social Security (card and benefits), Veterans (medical, educational), Nutritional Awareness, Job Search Workshops.

WHY RESEARCH AT CRC?

There were a number of primary reasons for conducting these two studies at CRC. First, the facility, which is one of the country's largest institutions for civil committed drug users, is operated by the State of California and has served as a model for other state civil commitment programs.

Second, the treatment philosophy at CRC derives, in general, from the principles of "the therapeutic community". Although, anyone familiar with the total institutional setting at CRC will quickly note that CRC is in fact operated as a correctional facility. In fact, it is a medium security facility with a staff of 1000. CRC has the capacity for 5,000 males and 1,200 females, who are housed in separate units. CRC has 50 dormitories with 100 beds per dorm.

Because a CRC commitment is involuntary it may, in fact, be advantageous to the criminal addicts. According to a recent government report:

> Clearly, relying on the addict alone to initiate treatment is insufficient. When treatment is voluntary, the addict is in the driver's seat. Decisions about whether and when to start treatment, and when to stop it, are entirely up to him. Many addicts seek treatment in detoxification facilities on a "revolving door" basis: they return periodically to reduce their drug habit to more manageable, and more affordable proportions. Over half of those who enter therapeutic communities drop out before completing the program. In methadone treatment programs for heroin addiction, urine monitoring often shows that the addicts are not taking the methadone, or are taking illegal drugs other than heroin. Addicts who drop out of treatment and addicts who are permitted continued drug use are in fact being inadequately treated (8).

Third, the rehabilitation statistics from CRC concerning its programs of education, personal counseling, and vocational services, have shown that as many as 35 percent of first releases were "clean" one year after release from the institution. Although only 16 percent of these first releases remained free of drugs three years after release, CRC does compare better than most other programs in the country.

Finally, detailed psychological studies of CRC's drug user population are desperately lacking. The writer could locate only several other in depth psychological investigations of the facility conducted during its 30 year history. The result of these two studies on locus of control and self-concept help to fill this hiatus.

In addition to the evaluation of the CRC drug user's personality, it is also of importance to characterize the drug user's behavior prior to their admission for rehabilitation. An important follow-up study conducted by the University of North Carolina (9) presents useful patient background information preceding drug treatment. This descriptive material is presented in Tables 4 and 5.

As part of this writer's two investigations, essential pre-arrest/treatment biographical information was also gathered. These results are presented in Tables 6 through 9.

Table 4		
Patient Behavior in the Year Preceding Admission to Treatment		
	Type of Treatment		
Behavior	Outpatient (Methadone)	Outpatient (Non-Methadone)	Therapeutic Community
	%	%	%
Serious Criminal Activity	33	37	60
Illegal activity as primary source of income	23	12	34
Fully employed(40 weeks or more)	24	24	15
Heavy alcohol use	25	36	42
Suicidal thoughts or attempts	29	48	44
Multiple drug related problems (3 or more)	41	50	63

Table 5		
Selected Characteristics of Drug Treatment Patients		
	Type of Treatment		
	Outpatient	Outpatient	Residential
Characteristic	(Methadone)	(Non-Methadone)	
	%	%	%
Previous treatment for drug abuse	75	34	53
Referral through the criminal justice system	3	31	31
Public assistance as the source of income	24	14	11
Private health insurance coverage	17	28	14

Table 6		
DEMOGRAPHIC BACKGROUND DATA		
CRC FIRST OFFENDERS (1970)		
AGE 18 - 26		
	Ethnicity		
	White	Mexican-American	Black
Mean Age	22	23	21.5
Mean Education (Years)	11.4	10.5	10.3
Marital Status			
Single	5	1	
Married	1	4	2
Divorced			3
Separated		1	1
Common Law			
Not Reporting	1	1	
Religious Preference			
Catholic	2	5	1
Protestant	4		4
Jewish			
Other		1	2
Not Reporting	1	1	

Table 6 *Cont.*		
Mean Time of Drug Use		
Years	2.5	1.8	3.0
Time of Prior Institutionalization		
Months	7	12	15
First Drug Used		
Cocaine	3	1	1
Marijuana	10	12	13
Speed	2	2	1
Hallucinogen			
Opiate			
Other	1		1
Not Reporting			

Table 7

DEMOGRAPHIC BACKGROUND DATA

CRC FIRST OFFENDERS (1970)

AGE 27 - 35

	Ethnicity		
	White	Mexican-American	Black
Mean Age	28	29	31
Mean Education (Years)	11.6	9.7	10.4
Marital Status			
Single	1	1	
Married	2	5	2
Divorced	2		3
Separated	1	1	
Common Law			1
Not Reporting	1		1
Religious Preference			
Catholic	2	6	2
Protestant	1	1	1
Jewish	2		
Other			
Not Reporting	2		4

Table 7 *Cont.*			
Mean Time of Drug Use			
Years	4.5	5.0	6.7
Time of Prior Institutionalization			
Months	14	14	27
First Drug Used			
Cocaine	2	1	2
Marijuana	12	13	14
Speed	2	2	
Hallucinogen			
Opiate			
Other			
Not Reporting			

Table 8		
DEMOGRAPHIC BACKGROUND DATA		
CRC FIRST OFFENDERS (1990)		
AGE 18 - 26		
	Ethnicity		
	White	Mexican-American	Black
Mean Age	22.5	24.0	24.0
Mean Education (Years)	11.7	11.6	10.1
Marital Status			
Single	3	1	
Married	2	5	2
Divorced			3
Separated			1
Common Law			
Not Reporting	2	1	1
Religious Preference			
Catholic	3	5	
Protestant	3	8	4
Jewish			
Other	1		8
Not Reporting		2	3

Table 8 *Cont.*			
Mean Time of Drug Use			
Years	3.6	2.7	4.6
Time of Prior Institutionalization			
Months	24	20	27
First Drug Used			
Cocaine	1	1	2
Marijuana	14	13	14
Speed	1	2	
Hallucinogen			
Opiate			
Other			
Not Reporting		1	

Table 9		
DEMOGRAPHIC BACKGROUND DATA		
CRC FIRST OFFENDERS (1990)		
AGE 27 - 35		
	Ethnicity		
	White	Mexican-American	Black
Mean Age	28.3	30.3	33.4
Mean Education (Years)	11.7	10.7	11.1
Marital Status			
Single		1	
Married		4	
Divorced	4		3
Separated	2	1	2
Common Law			
Not Reporting	1		2
Religious Preference			
Catholic	1	4	
Protestant			2
Jewish			
Other			
Not Reporting	6	3	4

Table 9 *Cont.*		
Mean Time of Drug Use		
Years	5.3	7.6	8.3
Time of Prior Institutionalization		
Months	24	30	33
First Drug Used		
Cocaine	1	1	1
Marijuana	14	13	15
Speed		2	
Hallucinogen			
Opiate			
Other	1		
Not Reporting			

CHAPTER II

REFERENCES

1. STRAUS N. *Addicts and Drug Abusers*, Twayne, New York, 1971, pp. 69-70.

2. DUSTER, T. *The Legislation of Morality*. The Free Press, Toronto, 1970, p. 134.

3. STATE OF CALIFORNIA, *All About the Addict Program*, 2-1988, p. 1.

4. DUSTER, T. *The Legislation of Morality*. The Free Press, Toronto, 1970, p. 134.

5. WOOD, R. W. "The Civil Narcotics Program". *Lincoln Law Rev.*, 1967, 2, pp. 116-138.

6. WOOD, R. W. "The Civil Narcotics Program". *Lincoln Law Rev.*, 1967, 2, pp.116-138.

7. CRC - Civil Addict Program Casework Guideline, State California, 1990, p. 61.

8. NATIONAL DRUG CONTROL STRATEGY, U. S. Government Printing Office, 1989, p. 41.

9. DRUG ABUSE TREATMENT, University of North Carolina Press, 1989.

CHAPTER III

LOCUS OF CONTROL AND SELF-CONCEPT -
WHAT ARE THEY?

The Locus of Control Dimension - Who's In Charge?

In the spring of 1981, after President Reagan was shot by would-be assassin, John Hinkley, ex-general and Secretary of State, Alexander Haig, made his one great political gaff. Via a national television-press conference Mr. Haig declared to the waiting American public that "I'm in charge here" (meaning the White House). The problem, of course, was that he wasn't! The psychological concept locus of control relates directly to how much a person perceives he/she is in control of his/her life.

As a psychological variable, locus of control came from the scholarly work of social psychologist, Rotter, who provided the necessary theoretical base in his social learning theory model. Rotter conceptualized locus or control as a generalized expectancy of reinforcement based on prior experience and learning. He held it to be of major importance in relation to performance in diverse social learning situations. He maintained that "consistent individual differences exist among individuals in the degree to which they are likely to attribute personal control to reward in the same situation" (1). Rotter succinctly defined locus of control in the following way:

> When a reinforcement is perceived by the subject as following some action of his own but not being

entirely contingent upon his action, then, in our culture, it is typically perceived as the result of luck, chance, fate, as under the control of powerful others, or an unpredictable because of the great complexity of the forces surrounding him. When the event is interpreted in this way by an individual, we have labeled this a belief in external control. If the person perceives that the event is contingent upon his own behavior or his own relatively permanent characteristics, we have termed this a belief in internal control (2).

Stated another way, locus of control pertains to the amount of perceived control individuals have over the events controlling their lives. Some people feel they have almost complete control over their destiny. These people are internal on locus of control. Other people feel they have very little control over their lives and are characterized as external on locus of control. In a sense, locus of control relates to the personal power we believe we have to manage our lives or to manage our reactions to diverse social-psychological situations. The locus of control dimension has been related to such factors as autonomy, competence, beliefs about fate, chance or luck, power and both self-concept and self-confidence (3).

Measurement of Locus of Control

The generally acceptable instrument used to measure a person's locus of control orientation and the instrument used in this investigation is the Rotter Internality-Externality Scale, or simply the IE Scale. Rotter and his colleagues developed this important IE scale in order to ascertain whether the controlling events of human behavior lie inside or outside of the individual. The complete IE Scale appears in Appendix I.

The first attempt to devise such an IE scale was done by Phares in the mid 1950's. He studied chance, fate, and luck on personal perception of power (4). Phares' pioneer work was then followed by other revisions of the IE scale. Other psychologists undertook to broaden this IE instrument through the construction of new subscales such as achievement, affection and social and political attitudes. They also introduced a control index for social desirability.

Critical to the present investigation is the degree to which social desirability affects IE scores, especially among various deviant groups, such as hospitalized drug users. The results of several investigations conducted with federal prison inmates have demonstrated a high correlation between the IE and social desirability (5). The average IE score for prisoners was significantly more internal than the college students, although the reverse trend would normally be expected. The question of whether social desirability is or is not a potentially complicating factor in locus of control research with drug users is certainly worthy of examination.

The final Rotter IE scale used in this investigation is comprised of 29 forced-choice items. Ten examples are:

- Many times we might as well decided what to do by flipping a coin.

- Children get into trouble because their parents punish them too much.

- The trouble with most children nowadays is that their parents are too easy with them.

- Many of the unhappy things in people's lives are partly due to bad luck.

- People's misfortunes result from the mistakes they make.

- It is usually best to cover up one's mistakes.

- Most misfortunes are the result of lack of ability, ignorance, laziness, or all three.

- Many times I feel that I have little influence over the things that happen to me.

- There's not much use in trying too hard to please people. If they like you, they like you.

- Sometimes I feel that I don't have much control over the direction my life is taking.

Prior Locus of Control Studies

Gore and Rotter found that scores on the I-E scale related directly to social action taking behavior; e.g., persons who were inclined to see themselves as determiners of their own fate and who tended to align themselves with personal and decisive social action were internal (6).

Strickland, who extensively studied the locus of control dimension especially with college students, reported findings in agreement with Gore and Rotter's. She demonstrated that students committed to social protest movements, social action takers, were more internal than the non-involved students (7).

One study done by Williams and Nickels showed that internal people see themselves as clever, efficient, ambitious, assertive, dependable, organized and reasonable. On the other hand, external individuals indicated self-pitying and negative responses. External scorers were also seen as prone to more frequent accidents and had suicidal thoughts more than internal scorers (8). Tolor and Reznikoff concluded that external college students showed a high tendency toward death anxiety (9).

Locus of control studies in the field of criminal psychology have dealt with a number of deviant groups. For example, Ladwig sampled the locus of control of a group of federal prisoners, age 18 to 26, and found these offenders high on measures of externality (10). In a later study, Lefcourt and Ladwig investigated internal-external orientations of sixty Black and sixty White inmates who were selected from two correctional facilities. The subjects did not differ significantly on measures of social class, age, intelligence, or reasons for incarceration. The results indicated that a significantly larger percentage of Black inmates were external compared with the Whites (11). Franklin, who sampled one thousand individuals on locus of control, also found that socio-economic class and locus of control were related; i.e., members of the lower socio-economic classes tended to be somewhat more external; i.e. saw their lives as being controlled by outside forces (12).

In another prison study correlating locus of control with self-concept, Fitts and Hamner found that prisoners with favorable self-concepts manifested a correspondent internal locus of control and vice-versa for low self-concept scores (13). These results corroborated the results of an earlier investigation of locus of control conducted by Richard (14). He studied the self-concept of institutionalized delinquents and concluded that delinquents with poor self-concepts also reflected an external locus of control. On the other hand, Richard suggested that delinquents with positive, well-defined self-concepts showed an internal locus of control. Seeman also reported that prisoners reflected an external locus of control (15). Patterson has related external locus of control to personal depression (16).

In summary, although the emergence of locus of control is a rather recent addition to personality theory, this dimension holds promise for better enabling psychologists to understand and interpret the behavior of deviant groups. Rotter's pioneer work on this dimension, especially the development of the Rotter IE Scale, remains the definitive work on the subject. The Rotter IE scale has been used extensively with many divergent behavioral groups, including a number of prison applications; thus it was chosen as the instrument of choice in the two CRC investigations.

Ethnicity, Socio-Economic Class and Locus of Control

Several locus of control investigations, Lefcourt and Ladwig, (17), Battle and Rotter (18), and Franklin (19) found ethnicity to be a potentially confounding variable for investigations of this dimension. Battle and Rotter (20) reported that lower-class Black school children were considerably more external than middle-class Blacks or upper or lower classWhites. The Lefcourt and Ladwig study (21), which measured locus of control among comparable age groups of Black and White prisoners, reported that the Blacks were significantly higher on externality. It is apparent from these studies that ethnicity does affect locus of control measures and it was taken into account in this study.

Measurement of Socio-Economic Class Position

Investigations also have reported that socio-economic class tends to affect the locus of control variable (22). In light of these findings this study checked for possible socio-economic differences between both the first and recidivist offenders and the younger and older offenders. This was achieved by presenting all subjects the self-administered Warner Index of Status Characteristics (ISC). In order to determine socio-economic class Warner devised four status characteristics: occupation of father, source of income, house type and dwelling area. Appendix III presents the scales for rating these four characteristics.

To obtain each subject's ISC the ratings were multiplied by the following assigned weights:

Occupation	4
Source of Income	3
House Type	3
Dwelling Area	2

After the ratings were multiplied by the assigned factor, social class equivalents were established:

Upper and Middle Class	34 and less
Lower-Middle Class	40 - 55
Upper-Lower Class	56 - 67
Lower-Lower Class	68 - 84

Self-Concept - Who Am I?

The term self or self-concept is one of the most distinctive and well-researched constructs in American social-psychology. Attention to and recognition of the term extends back almost a century. James (23), in his chapter on the self, served to introduce the term into American psychology. Much of the substantive data regarding the self-concept, even as it is used in contemporary theory, derives from James' work.

Between 1910 and 1940 the field of psychology, dominated by the behaviorist and functionalist philosophies, did not attribute much emphasis to the self as these theories were unable to account for this mentalistic construct (24). Self theory, according to Lazarus (25) "tended to have its greatest impact in the middle of the twentieth century, particularly in clinical psychology...". Raimy's (26) research of the self-concept marks the beginning of the application of the social scientific approach to the study of self. Many of the definitional properties ascribed to the self-concept come from Raimy's investigation. After the appearance of his work, "a whole series of writings and research projects have been completed using this concept as a basis (27), (28)."

Hall and Linzey (29) have pointed out that in modern psychology the self-concept has come to have two distinct meanings: the self as an object and the self as process. In their view, both uses of the term strive to account for and measure various phenomena as well as permit one to conceptualize observations of certain aspects of one's own behavior. However, the self-concept has been defined in various ways by many writers who have used the term within their own theoretical frameworks. For example, the self-concept has been formulated in terms of social interaction theory (30); in terms of Gestalt theory (31); in terms of field theory (32), and still in terms of phenomonology (33), (34). While these psychologists do differ on their theoretical interpretations of the self-concept (35), most self theorists believe that the researcher cannot understand or predict human action without feedback or personal knowledge of the subject's conscious perceptions of the environment and of his self-concept in relation to the environment. Moreover, self theorists contend that an individual's experiences are best understood when introduced into direct awareness or consciousness.

Self-concept, as employed in this investigation, rests on the contemporary approach advanced by Rogers (36). Rogers, a leading psychologist, has devoted a great deal of his professional career to redefining the self-concept. Rogers noted that an individual's behavior can be evaluated only from his own observational, subjective vantage point. Rogers' theory of self is based on his therapeutic encounters and as such it is not surprising that many of his self-concept and self propositions refer to subjective observable responses recorded during therapy (37).

The basic elements of Rogers' self theory include the person as an organism, the phenomenal field, which is the totality of experience; and the self, which is the differentiated portion of the phenomenal field consisting of a pattern of conscious perceptions and values of the "I" and "me (38)."

In the Rogers self theory the here and now existential experiences are considered to be of central importance. Historical factors in an individual's life are important from the standpoint of personal adjustment only to the extent to which they bear on the individual's phenomenal field (39). Although a leading phenomenologist, Rogers does not attempt to refute the importance of unconscious personality factors.

Measurement of Self-Concept

Raimy's (40) observation that certain positive changes in self-concept took place in the process of psychotherapy led to the emergence of self-concept as an important variable in the psychotherapeutic literature

(41). In the attempt to measure self-concept, a number of different instruments and more generalized techniques have been developed. Strong and Feder reported that at least 15 instruments and techniques have been developed to tap this dimension. They stated: "Eleven of the fifteen techniques give some type of perceived self-concept score; seven of them utilize an adjustment index of some sort."

Wylie (42), who also reviewed the literature on self-concept scaling techniques, reported that there are many highly effective methods for self-concept investigation. The Osgood Semantic Differential Technique, SD, (43) served as the self-concept instrument for these investigations.

A central hypothesis underlying the SD is that essential components of the meaning of certain topical concepts, e.g., religion, democratic party or the self-concept, can be assessed by tabulating ratings of the concept on a number of antipodal adjective scales. On the SD each set of these antipodal adjectives constitutes a scale (44). In the original Osgood study (45) fifty such adjectival rating scales were factor analyzed, yielding three general factors of meaning: potency, activity and evaluation.

The SD is essentially a combination of controlled associations and scaling procedures. Each subject is provided with a topical concept to be differentiated and a set of bipolar adjectival scales. In this case self-concept was the rated topic. The subject is requested to indicate for each item (paring of a concept with a scale) the direction of his association and its intensity on a seven point scale. The subject is to rate or mark the scale according to how close he feels the topical concept is to either end of the opposite words. Table 1, designed by the writer, shows a theoretical rating of self-concept. Each subject in the 1970 investigation was given a copy of the SD containing nine rating scales or pairs of antipodal adjectives with seven blank spaces between them. The subject's task was to indicate for each item the direction of his association and its intensity in accordance with how closely he felt the concept was to either of the opposite words given. For scoring purposes the seven blanks were assigned numerical values of plus one through plus seven and a total score was obtained by summing the scales. Nine of the scales are presented:

	1	2	3	4	5	6	7	
Clean								Dirty
Fast								Slow
Strong								Weak
Large								Small
Active								Passive
Valuable								Worthless
Tasty								Distasteful
Hot								Cold
Deep								Shallow

The Osgood Semantic Differential Technique used at CRC with instructions is presented in Appendix II.

Prior Studies of Self-Concept

It was noted that the self-concept dimension has provided a meaningful experimental variable for more than three decades. Unlike the less extensive literature on locus of control, there has been a voluminous outpouring of data from self-concept studies. A comprehensive review of these investigations is beyond the scope of this study. Wylie (46) and Strong and Feder (47) both have produced replete summary studies of self-concept research, including an analysis of the scales and techniques for assessment.

The studies included here were chosen specifically from the field of criminology. Several investigations pertaining to self-concepts of juvenile delinquents and prisoners have been reported. A difficulty arises in comparing these studies because virtually every investigation used a different measuring instrument or technique. Fitts and Hamner (48) pointed out the problem using different measurements: "Often, these instruments were hastily devised, poorly standardized, and provided only limited information about the self-concepts of the subjects." Reckless (49) investigated self-concepts of youths in high delinquency areas. His work was the first major study of self-concept among juvenile delinquents. In formulating his containment theory of juvenile delinquency causation, Reckless attempted to account for a variety of social and psychological factors, including self-concept.

85

Reckless worked from the premise that it was feasible to identify various components that allow certain juveniles to develop or maintain non-delinquent habits and adjustment patterns, while other juveniles from the same ecological area develop pro-delinquent patterns. He wrote:

> Finally, there is a strong suspicion that a well-developed concept of self as a "good boy" is the component which keeps middle- and upper-class boys who live in better neighborhoods out of delinquency. The point is that this component seems to be strong enough to "insulate" the adolescent against delinquency in the unfavorable neighborhoods (50).

Reckless' pioneer self-concept work was carried further by investigators who isolated specific characteristics of delinquents' self-concepts. Several investigators found differences on measures of self-concept between first offender and recidivist juvenile delinquents (51),(52). Balester and Lefeber's studies sought to demonstrate self-concept differences between first and recidivist institutionalized juvenile offenders. The research design used by Balester served as a model for the present investigation. Balester examined the differences in self-concept between first offenders and recidivists while comparing a nondelinquent group. Balester wrote: "...there is a significant difference between the means of the recently incarcerated first offenders and already incarcerated repeaters. The former group has a more positive score than the latter. The mean positive score of the first offenders is higher than the mean positive score of the repeaters" (53).

Fitts and Hamner (54) summarized Balester's results: "Delinquent individuals and nondelinquent individuals are, of course, exhibiting different behavior patterns and, therefore, should have significantly different self-concept organizations." Lefeber also hypothesized self-concept differences between a first offender group and a comparable recidivist delinquent group. The basic design used in his investigation was similar to the research design followed in the present study except that Lefeber employed a matched control group. His results suggested that there are significant differences on self-concept between first offenders and recidivists. In summarizing his study, Lefeber wrote:

> On all measures of self-concept, the most extreme differences were consistently found between the non-delinquent and recidivist groups. Lower scores obtained by the delinquent recidivists indicate that a high degree of self-devaluation among this population (55).

In two additional reported studies Fitts and Hamner reported differences between first offenders and recidivists with delinquent groups. In one study of a youth correctional facility in Tennessee they found that

recidivists "are consistently more deviant than first offenders on virtually all scores with quite sizable differences on some--especially the (positive) scores (56)." Additionally, they compared self-concept data with the
Lefeber material and reported a similarity of findings.
While their findings followed the same general trend and
direction, it should be pointed out that the contrast between first offenders and recidivists was not as sharp as
in the Balester or Lefeber investigations.

A number of self-concept investigations of juvenile
delinquents and criminals have noted that these groups
are maladjusted or behaviorally disturbed. Implicit in
these investigations is the suggestion that perhaps treatment programs might be aimed at self-concept improvement. A review of the self-concept literature in criminology served to locate a single investigation designed to
improve the self-concept for juvenile delinquents. Cole,
Oetting and Miskimins (57) report the findings of a relatively restricted group treatment program for delinquent
girls. These writers reported that the program proved
efficacious:

> It would appear that these girls became more
> self-reflective, open and spontaneous. Because of
> the nonspecific nature of the measure used, some
> evidence is provided in support of the contention
> that these changes in self-concept were very likely
> global.

The results of the Cole study have potential for wide implications for other treatment agencies. As an example, one could conceivably replicate such an investigation at CRC or a similar institution.

Cohen noted that an inmate's self-concept tends to become less favorable as a function of the length of incarceration. Whereas Cohen's findings were inconsistent with those of Cole, his general trends lent support to the Balester-Lefeber work. Kennedy (58) investigated the effect of prisonization on self-concept of men in a medium security prison. His results showed that the length of incarceration and prisonization were positively correlated with low self-concepts. Deitz (59) reported significant differences on measures of self-concept between a delinquent sample and non-delinquent controls. He concluded that delinquents manifest a greater degree of self-dissatisfaction than do the non-delinquents.

Hurley compared self-concepts and the discrepancy between real and ideal self-concepts of criminals and non-criminals. According to Hurley (60), "Criminals reflected a mean lower than noncriminals, indicating that the former conceives of himself as being less socially adapted than the latter." Hurley's research further strengthened the relationship between negative self-concept formation and offenders status.

Fitts and Hamner summarized major findings pertaining to self-concept and delinquency investigations. The delinquent was characterized as follows:

1. He is apt to be rather uncertain in his picture of himself.

2. He has difficulty defining himself and is easily influenced by external suggestion. In this sense he is easily influenced by his environment and tends to turn outward for control and evaluation of his own behavior.

3. His self-concept is confused and characterized by many conflicting and contradictory perceptions of himself.

4. Delinquents' self-concepts are similar to those of other groups also characterized by antisocial behavior, e.g., alcoholics, sociopathic personalities, and sexual deviants.

5. There is no evidence that incarceration alone produces any significant improvement in self-concept.

6. Subjects who became recidivists after leaving an institution, showed little self-concept change during treatment.

7. Subjects who respond best to treatment programs
have higher initial self-concepts than those who
do not respond well (61).

The foregoing review has pointed out that there are
self-concept differences between first offenders and
recidivists. Moreover, these differences indicate that
recidivists have less favorable measures of self-concept.
A goal in this investigation was to measure the self-concepts of institutionalized drug users divided into first
offenders and recidivists. It was predicted, as was the
case in the juvenile delinquent research, that the
recidivists would have more unfavorable measures of
self-concept than first offender drug users. Furthermore,
it was predicted that older (27-35 years) subjects for both
first and recidivist offender status would report significantly less favorable measures of self-concept than
younger subjects.

Self-Concept Studies of Drug Addicts

While there is extensive literature pertaining to the
self-concept of prisoners, juvenile delinquents and other
institutionalized populations, a paucity of available investigations directly concern the self-concepts of drug
users. That drug users come to think of themselves in
negativistic terms has been documented by several investigators (62), (63), (64). Clinard (65) contended that in
becoming addicted the individual must necessarily

modify and develop new ways of looking at himself. Lindesmith (66) noted from self-report data that it is not uncommon for drug users to characterize themselves in pejorative, depreciating terminology.

In an analysis of these negative statements Lindesmith wrote:

> Addicts refer to themselves as "junkies" or "users" and are so regarded by others. Frequently, in a jocular sense, they use the more expressive term "dope fiend".

Ausubel (67) also reported that opiate users have unfavorable measures of self-concept. He reasoned further that lack of self-concept and self-esteem is the product of unsatisfactory parent-child relationships resulting from parental rejection. Casriel, in agreement with Ausubel, argued that adult drug addicts manifest unfavorable self images which are the product of a great deal of anxiety during childhood. He wrote, "Secondary addicts have suffered a great deal of anxiety in childhood. They tend to be withdrawn, depressed, personally isolated, and uncommunicative as children, adolescents and adults (68)."

Birner (69) studied the level of self esteem of a group of institutionalized drug users who, in addition to using heroin, ingested a variety of non-opiate drugs. He concluded that the longer the duration of drug use the greater the chance that the addict would accept a deviant value system.

Schiff's (70) investigation stands out as the most well- controlled and definitive study of the self-concept of drug users. Schiff carefully evaluated measures of self-concept and self-esteem as well as discrepancy scores among a group of institutionalized drug users and compared these findings with a population of noncriminals and non-users. He studied two addict groups: 1) individuals whose addiction developed in adolescence and, 2) individuals whose addiction developed in adulthood. A central finding of his study was that adults who had become addicted as teenagers remain as teenagers in terms of measured levels of self-esteem. The adults addicted during adulthood revealed more extreme patterns of maladjustment. Schiff's results indicated further that maladjustment increases as a function of the age when a person becomes addicted.

Chein, using a projective technique, measured the projected self-image of adolescent opiate addicts. He found that the stories told by the addicts involved psychological (TAT) themes which portend unfavorable self images. These involved murder, rape, strangulation, terminal cancer, feelings of rotting away, failure and impotence (71).

It is difficult to make cross-study comparisons of these investigations specifically designed to measure the self-concept of drug addicts. While certain investigations have been concerned with the self-concept image of adolescent drug users, other research has dealt specifically with an older population, as in the case of the Schiff study. Chein and Ausubel concurred that strained family interactions are a prime etiological factor responsible for the addict's generally unfavorable self-concept. Whereas these researchers concerned themselves with the identification of the casual factors underscoring the drug users' unfavorable self-concepts, other investigators directed little attention to the etiology issue.

In summary, self-concept studies of drug users appear to suggest that: 1) drug users generally have self-concepts like other deviant populations; 2) drug users have less favorable measures of self-concept; 3) identity and self-image problems associated with the drug users may originate from a deterioration of parent-child relationships; 4) drug users who began using narcotics during adulthood, as opposed to adolescence, have less favorable measures of self-concept; 5) sex-identity diffusion might play a significant role in drug users' attenuated self-concept.

Ethnicity, Socio-Economic Class and Self-Concept

Whereas ethnicity is a clear factor with locus of control, in self-concept investigations, however, the effect of ethnicity is not as clear for there is some conflicting evidence. Although the self-concept is apparently not as profoundly affected by ethnicity as the locus of control, it seemed reasonable in the present study to match the first and recidivist samples in ethnicity. This was accomplished by sub-dividing the whole CRC research sample into three equal sized (N = 16) groups, White, Mexican-Americans and Blacks.

Investigations of drug addicts have revealed distinct drug patterning differences among ethnic groups . It has been further noted that there are certain personality differences among ethnic groups (72).

Investigations also have reported that socio-economic class tends to affect both locus of control (73) and self-concept (74). In light of the findings, this study was checked for possible socio-economic differences between both the first and recidivist offenders and the younger and older offenders. This was achieved by presenting all subjects the self-administered Warner Index of Status Characteristics (ISC) (1960). The ISC is presented, with instructions, in Appendix III.

Locus of Control and Self-Concept with Drug Users

After a lengthy review of locus of control and self-concept studies, it was noticed that studies with drug users have been somewhat absent from the psychological literature. This was especially true of the previous studies conducted at CRC. The writer's interest in studying the psychodynamics of drug users has remained persistent throughout the past 20 years.

After a review of a number of articles pertaining to the rehabilitation of drug offenders at CRC, the writer's interest culminated in a first study (75) of locus of control and self-concept among a sample of CRC drug offenders. The initial research proposal was submitted to the CRC research staff in 1970. It was made clear that the research there was to evaluate the effects of drug offender status (first or recidivist) and age on locus of control and self-concept only. The 1990 research sample was selected in a similar manner to the 1970 sample. Due to time management needs, the professional staff at CRC administered the 1990 scales to the drug offender groups.

During a first visit to CRC, two residents, who expressed a serious and continuing interest in the study, were solicited by the writer to serve as research assistants. These residents were advised, pursuant to the CRC research policy, that they might help administer the test instruments and gather other demographic data in the research sample. Both of these residents had previous experience in the administration and scoring of psychological tests in correctional institutions, and demonstrated a knowledge of general testing procedure.

During the two studies, in order to insure that two equal samples of first and recidivist CRC residents divided into two equal age groups and three equal ethnic groups would be formed, data was collected from 110 residents. The writer and the CRC research staff assistants scheduled three testing sessions, two in the morning and one in the afternoon. During each session approximately 35 residents were tested. All testing was conducted in quiet classrooms. During these testing sessions the writer and assistantsadministered to the residents the locus of control I-E scale, Warner's ISC, a demographic background questionnaire, and the Carlson Personality Survey (CPS) (1990 administration). The CPS measures a number of psychological traits including chemical abuse and self-concept. It was felt that the CPS was an ideal test to assess self-concept with institutionalized drug users. This particular test was not available for the 1970 study.

As part of the instructions it was made clear to the CRC residents that participation in this study was on a voluntary basis and all data would be held in strict confidence, and in an attempt to preserve anonymity all residents were asked not to sign the research instruments or in any way identify themselves. Furthermore, it was made clear that the research was not associated with CRC or the State of California.

Locus of Control and Self-Concept Predictions

On the premise that research involving the locus of control and self-concept variables had the potential for enabling us to better understand the dynamics of the drug user and to better cope with the raging drug dilemma, this researcher devised two investigations (1970 and 1990) to assess locus of control and self-concept among first admissions and recidivist drug users committed to CRC. The following seven predictions concerning locus of control and self-concept were made:

1. CRC drug abuse recidivists, when compared with a matched sample of first offenders, will rate or see themselves significantly more external on locus of control.

2. Older (27-35 years) CRC drug abusers will show significantly more externality than younger (18 to 26 years) subjects.

3. Social economic class position is related to measure of locus of control.

4. CRC drug abuse recidivists, when compared with a matched sample of first offenders, will rate or see themselves significantly less favorable on self-concept.

5. Older (27-35 years) CRC drug abusers will show significantly lower self-concept than younger (18 to 26 years) subjects.

6. Social economic class position is related to measures of self-concept.

7. Locus of control and self-concept are significantly and positively related.

The final prediction made in this study concerned the relationship between locus of control and self-concept. In examination of the literature, it was ascertained that these two important psychological variables have not been previously correlated.

Four psychological tests were used in this investigation: (1) the Rotter Internal-External Scale,(I-E) (76) for locus of control assessment, (2) the Warner Index of Status Characteristics (ISC) to determine socioeconomic status (77), (3) the Carlson Psychological Survey(CPS) (78), and (4) the Osgood Semantic Differential to Measure self-concept (SD) (79).

The second instrument, the Warner Index of Status Characteristics (ISC), is one of several scales designed to measure social economic class (SEC). Previous research suggested that social economic class is a confounding variable for locus of control research. Because of these studies, it seemed reasonable to assume that the social economic status should be controlled in this investigation.

The third scale, the Carlson Psychological Survey (CPS), was selected as an additional technique of choice to measure self-concept, in combination with the semantic differential (SD), during the 1990 study. The CPS was thought to have special applicability for use at CRC with drug users. According to Carlson, who developed the CPS test, the following conclusions were made:

> Among the many personality scales and inventories, there is a conspicuous dearth of tests intended primarily for individuals failing under the aegis of the criminal justice system. Those instruments commonly employed on this population have typically been developed on psychiatric or hospital samples. Questionnaires standardized on irrelevant groups are probably neither appropriate nor useful for this population.
>
> Many psychological trait scales have the additional problem of semantic difficulty relative to the poor reading skills of many persons in trouble with the law. Many such individuals do not have good academic records and report difficulty in comprehending personality test items. Also, those individuals who do have difficulty reading are commonly overwhelmed by long tests with

hundreds of items. Test developers have attempted to deal with this problem by eliminating less valuable items and shortening their tests, but they are restrained by the number of items necessary to maintain scale reliability.

Another problem, not restricted to the criminal inmate population, concerns the true-false item format. Many individuals appear to find it difficult to dichotomize their answers when a test item may be viewed as having varying degrees of veracity. Frustration at this forced dichotomy is regularly seen in such behaviors as writing answers in the columns of the answer sheets, marking both answers, and the frequent requesting of assistance from the examiner. That is, while the true-false format has many desirable psychometric advantages, it seems to lack certain administrative qualities.

Consideration of these problems suggested that an attempt be made to develop a psychometric instrument intended primarily for individuals accused or convicted of crimes, or otherwise referred for social deviant behavior. It was considered of primary importance that recognition be given to the unique situation of these individuals as well as the atypical reasons for referral. In addition, it was regarded as imperative that such a test make minimal literary demands

on the subjects without sacrificing the reliability
or amount of information available from the test
(80).

The results of the Carlson Psychological Survey will
be analyzed and appear as a separate study.

CHAPTER III

REFERENCES

1. ROTTER, J.B. *Social learning and clinical psychology.* Englewood Cliffs: Prentice-Hall, 1954.

2. ROTTER, J.B. Generalized expectancies for internal versus external control of reinforcement. Psychol. monogr., 1966, 80, P.I.

3. STRICKLAND, B. "Internal-external control expectancies". *Amer. Psychol.*, 1989, 44, pp. 1-7.

4. PHARES, E.J. "Expectancy changes in skill and chance situations". *J. Abnorm. Soc. Psychol.*, 1957, 54, pp. 339-342.

5. LADWIG, G.W. "Personal, situational and social determinants of preference for delayed reinforcement". Unpublished doctoral dissertation, Ohio State University, 1963.

6. GORE, P.M. and ROTTER, J.B. "A personality correlate of social action". *J. Pers.*, 1963, 31, pp. 58-64.

7. STRICKLAND, B. "The prediction of social action from a dimension of internal-external control". *J. Soc. Psychol.*, 1965, 66, pp. 353-358.

8. WILLIAMS, C.B. and NICKELS, J.B. "Internal-external control as related to accident and suicide proneness". *J. Consult. Clin. Psychol.*, **1969, 33, pp. 485-494.**

9. TOLOR, A. and REZNIKOFF, M. "Relation between insight, repression-sensitization, internal-external control, and death anxiety".*J. Abnorm. Psychol.*, **1967, 72, pp. 426-430.**

10. LADWIG, G.W. "Personal, situational and social determinants of preference for delayed reinforcement". Unpublished doctoral dissertation, Ohio State University, 1963.

11. LEFCOURT, H.M. and Ladwig, G.W. "The American Negro: a problem in expectancies". *J. Pers. Soc. Psychol.*, **1965, 1, pp. 377-380.**

12. FRANKLIN R.D. "Youth's expectancies about internal versus external control of reinforcement related to N variables". Unpublished doctoral dissertation, Purdue University, 1963.

13. FITTS, W.H. and HAMNER, W.T. The Tennessee self concept scale: ten years of research in mental health. Tennessee department of ment. health, 1961, 4, pp. 1-12.

14. RICHARD, W.C., MATES, C.G. and WHITTEN, L. "Personality traits and attitudes of adolescent girls with be-

havior disorders". Unpublished paper, presented at Southeastern Psychol. Associat., 1967.

15. SEEMAN, M. "Social learning theory and the theory of mass society". Unpublished paper presented at the American Social. Society, 1963.

16. PATTERSON, C. H. *Theories of counseling and psychotherapy.* New York: Harper and Row, Publishers, 1966.

17. LEFCOURT, H. M. and LADWIG, G. W. "The American Negro: a problem in expectancies". *J. pers. soc. Psychol.,* 1965, 1, pp. 377-380.

18. BATTLE, E. S. and ROTTER, J. B. "Children's feelings of personal control as related to social class and ethnic group". *J. Pers.,* 1963, 31, pp. 482-490.

19. FRANKLIN, R. D. "Youth's expectancies about internal versus external control of reinforcement related to N variables". Unpublished doctoral dissertation, Purdue University, 1963.

20. BATTLE, E. S. and ROTTER, J. B. "Children's feelings of personal control as related to social class and ethnic group"., *J. pers.* , 1963, 31, pp. 482-490.

21. LEFCOURT, H. M. and LADWIG, G. W. "The American Negro: a problem in expectancies". *J. pers. soc. Psychol.*, 1965, 1, pp. 377-380.

22. FRANKLIN, R. D. "Youth's expectancies about internal versus external control of reinforcement related to N variables". Unpublished doctoral dissertation, Purdue University, 1963.

23. JAMES, W. *Principles of psychology.* New York: Holt, 1890.

24. PHARES, E.J. "Expectancy changes in skill and chance situations". *J. Abnorm. Soc. Psychol.*, 1957, 54, pp. 339-342.

25. LAZARUS, R. S. *Adjustment and personality.* New York: McGraw-Hill Book Company, 1961.

26. RAIMEY, V.C. "The self-concept as a factor in counseling and personality". Unpublished doctoral dissertation. Ohio State University, 1948.

27. WYLIE, R. C. *The self-concept.* Nebraska: University of Nebraska Press, 1961.

28. LEFCOURT, H.M. and LADWIG, G.W. "The American Negro: a problem in expectancies". *J. pers. soc. Psychol.*, 1965, 1, pp. 377-380.

29. HALL, C. and LINZEY, G. *Theories of personality*. New York: Wiley, 1967.

30. MEAD, G. H. *Mind, self and society*. Chicago: University of Chicago Press, 1934.

31. KOFFKA, K. *Principles of gestalt psychology*. New York: Harcourt, 1935.

32. LEWIN, K. *Principles of topological psychology*. New York: McGraw, 1936.

33. RAIMEY, V. C. "The self-concept as a factor in counseling and personality". Unpublished doctoral dissertation. Ohio State University, 1948.

34. SNYGG, D. and COMBS, A. W. *Individual behavior*. New York: Harper, 1949.

35. WYLIE, R. C. *The self concept*. Nebraska: University of Nebraska Press, 1961.

36. ROGERS, C. R. *Client centered therapy*. Cambridge: Riverside Press, 1951.

37. ROGERS, C. R. *Client centered therapy*. Cambridge: Riverside Press, 1951.

38. ROGERS, C. R. *Client centered therapy*. Cambridge: Riverside Press, 1951.

39. CADE, A. J. "The relationship between counselor-client cultural background similarity and counseling progress". Unpublished doctoral dissertation. Michigan State University, 1963.

40. RAIMEY, V. C. "The self-concept as a factor in counseling and personality. Unpublished doctoral dissertation". Ohio State University, 1948.

41. STRONG, DONALD J. and FEDER, D. D. "Measurement of the self-concept; a critique of the literature". *J. counsel. Psychol.*, 1961, 8, pp. 170-178.

42. WYLIE, R. C. *The self concept.* Nebraska: University of Nebraska Press, 1961.

43. OSGOOD, C. E., SUCI, G. J. and TANNENBAUM, P. H. *The measurement of meaning.* Urbana: Univ. of Illinois Press, 1957.

44. KRECH, D., CRUTCHFIELD, R. S. and BALLACHEY, E. *Individual in society.* New York: McGraw-Hill, 1962.

45. OSGOOD, C. E., SUCI, G. J. and TANNENBAUM, P. H. *The measurement of meaning.* Urbana: Univ. of Illinois Press, 1957.

46. WYLIE, R. C. *The self concept.* Nebraska: University of Nebraska Press, 1961.

47. STRONG, D. J. and FEDER, D. D. "Measurement of the self-concept; a critique of the literature". *J. counsel. Psychol.*, 1961, 8, pp. 170-178.

48. FITTS, W. H. and HAMNER, W. T. "The self concept and delinquency: studies on the self concept and rehabilitation". Nashville mental health center., 1969, 1, pp. 1-96.

49. RECKLESS, W. C., DINITZ, S. and KAY, B. "The self component in potential delinquency and potential non-delinquency". *Amer. social Rev.*, 1957, 22, pp. 566-570.

50. RECKLESS, W. C., DINITZ, S. and KAY, B. "The self component in potential delinquency and potential non-delinquency".*Amer. social Rev.*, 1957, 22, pp. 566-570.

51. BALESTER, R. J. "The self concept and juvenile delinquency". Unpublished doctoral dissertation. Vanderbilt University, 1956.

52. LEFBER, J. A. "The delinquent's self concept". Unpublished doctoral dissertation, University of Southern California, 1965.

53. BALESTER, R. J. "The self concept and juvenile delinquency". Unpublished doctoral dissertation. Vanderbilt University, 1956.

54. FITTS, W. H. and HAMNER, W. T. "The self concept and delinquency: studies on the self concept and rehabilitation". Nashville mental health center., 1969, 1, pp. 1-96.

55. LEBFER, J. A. "The delinquent's self concept". Unpublished doctoral dissertation, University of Southern California, 1965, pp. 135-136.

56. FITTS, W. H. and HAMNER, W. T. "The self concept and delinquency: studies on the self concept and rehabilitation". Nashville mental health center., 1969, 1, pp. 1-96.

57. COLE, E. W., OETTING, E. R. and MISKIMINS, R. W. "Self concept therapy for adolescent females". *J. abnorm. Psychol.*, 1969, 74, pp. 642-645.

58. KENNEDY, W. C. "Prisonization and self conception: a study of a medium security prison". Unpublished doctoral dissertation, University of California, Los Angeles, 1970.

59. DIETZ, G. E. "A comparison of delinquents with non-delinquents on self concept, self-acceptance and parental identification". *J. genet. Psychol.*, 1969, 115, pp. 285-295.

60. HURLEY, W. H. "A study of the self-concepts of criminals and non-criminals. Unpublished doctoral dissertation". The University of Oklahoma, 1961.

61.FITTS, W.H. and HAMNER, W.T. "The self concept and delinquency: studies on the self concept and rehabilitation". Nashville mental health center., 1969, 1, pp. 1-96.

62. D. CLINARD, M. B. *Sociology of deviant behavior.* New York: Holt, Rinehart and Winston, Inc., 1963.

63. CASRIEL, D. *So fair a house: the story of synanon.* New Jersey: Prentice-Hall, Inc., 1963.

64.STRIKER, G. *Kicking it.* New York: Pyramid Books, 1971.

65. CLINARD, M. B. *Sociology of deviant behavior.* New York: Holt, Rinehart and Winston, Inc., 1963.

66. LINDSMITH, A. *Addiction and opiates.* Chicago: Aldine Publishing Company., 1968.

67. AUSUBEL, D. P. *Drug Addiction: physiological, psychological and sociological aspects.* New York: Random House, Inc. 1965.

68. CASRIEL, D. *So fair a house: the story of synanon.* New Jersey: Prentice-Hall, Inc., 1963.

69. BIRNER, L. "Level of self-esteem of imprisoned addicted users of narcotics drugs". Unpublished doctoral dissertation. Yeshiva University, 1961.

70. SCHIFF, S. "A self-theory investigation of drug addiction in relation to age of onset". Unpublished doctoral dissertation. New York University, 1959.

71. CHEIN, I., GERARD, D.C., LEE, R.S., and ROSENFELD, E. *The Road to H.*, New York: Basic Books, 1964.

72. ROBINS, L. N. and MURPHY, G. E. "Drug use in a normal population of young Negro men". *Amer. J. pub. Health.*, 1967, 57, pp. 1580-1596.

73. LEWIS, J. M. and OSBERG, J. W. "Observations on institutional treatment of character disorders". *Amer. J. Orthopsychiat.*, 1958, 28, pp. 730-744.

74. KLAUSNER, S. Z. "Social class and self concept". *J. soc. Psychol.*, 1953, 38, pp. 201-205.

75. BRADY, J. C. "The Psychological Aspects of Drug Abuse", published by City/County San Francisco, 1973.

76. ROTTER, J.B., Generalized expectancies for internal versus external control of reinforcement. *Psychol. monogr .*, 1966, 80, pp. 1-27.

77. PHARES, E. J. "Expectancy changes in skill and chance situations". *J. abnorm. soc. psychol.*, 1957, 54, pp. 339-342.

78. WARNER, W. L., MEEKER, M. L. and EELLS, K. W. *Social class in America.* New York: Harper Torchbooks, 1960.

79. CARLSON, C. A. *The Carlson Psychological Survey - A Manual*, Ontario, CA 1982.

80. OSGOOD, C. E., SUCI, G. J. and TENNANBAUM, P. H. *The measurement of meaning.* Urbana: Univ. of Illinois Press, 1957.

CHAPTER IV

RESULTS

Putting the Pieces in Place

During the past twenty years drug treatment specialists have called for a comprehensive assessment of the psychological factors related to drug use in order to differentiate users from other deviant groups as well as the other groups from each other. During the past twenty years the global drug problem has worsened. A 1989 governmental report states:

Today's drug addicts are more challenging to treat than those of a decade ago. Mental illness or psychological disorders are common, as is the practice of using a variety of illegal drugs, not just one. A typical drug treatment patient may, for example, have a history of heroin, cocaine, and marijuana use, along with excessive use of alcohol. He may have taken these substances separately or in combinations. Young offenders in particular must be confronted with penalites that both deter them from future drug use and embarrass them among their peers. Today, many young drug offenders boast about their lenient treatment in the hands of the authorities and wear it as a badge of pride; corrections officials must make sure that when juveniles are caught using or selling drugs, their punishment becomes a source of shame. We need a mix of sanctions for juvenile drug use that includes school suspension, parental notification, postponement of driver's license eligibility, and extends to weekends of "community service" that involve arduous and unenviable public chores (1).

Drug users come to treatment with widely varying social and vocational skills. Some are successful professionals from stable family backgrounds. Many others, however, have known only poverty, drugs and crime since childhood. These patients need more than just treatment. They need a range of social services, counseling, medical treatment (especially for those with AIDS) and job training in order to fashion a productive life without drugs. If drug treatment facilities are to be genuinely effective, they must be prepared to bring these services to the addict, either by offering them directly or by arranging them through cooperation with other agencies (2)."

This writer has attempted to take on the challenge to better understand the personality of the drug user, and in order to do this, has conducted two psychological studies. These studies were undertaken in two separated segments over a 20 year period to assess two important psychological variables, locus of control and self-concept among a group of institutionalized drug users committed at CRC. In both studies the seven major predictions or hypotheses were:

1. CRC drug abuse recidivists, or experienced users, when compared with a matched sample of first offenders, will rate or see themselves significantly more external on locus of control.

2. Older (27-35 years) CRC drug abusers will show significantly more externality than younger (18 to 26 years) subjects.

3. Social economic class position is related to measures of locus of control.

4. CRC drug abuse recidivists, or experienced users, rate or see themselves significantly less favorable in self-concept than a matched sample of first offenders.

5. Older (27-35 years) CRC drug abusers will show significantly lower self-concept than younger (18 to 26 years) subjects.

6. Social economic class position is positively related to measures of self-concept.

7. Locus of control and self-concept are significantly and positively related.

Implications of These Research Results

In this writer's view, the implications of this research have primary relevance in three specific areas:

1. These psychological findings on locus of control and self-concept may be applied toward development of differential therapeutic hospital treatment programs for drug offenders.

2. This investigation suggested that changes in the locus of control and self-concept of drug offenders is an important psychological variable which can be included as a central criterion for determination of drug offender release.

3. This research is germane for the determination of differential post-release practices for drug offenders after reinstatement in the community.

The results presented here compare the earlier 1970 CRC self-concept and locus of control ratings with the 1990 ratings. A central reason for conducting the follow-up study was to determine whether there would be any similarity between the two sets of scores. Each of the research predictions are discussed (I-VII) below.

I.First Versus Experienced Drug Users - Locus of Control Results

The first prediction in this study was that CRC drug abuse recidivists, when compared with a matched sample of first drug offenders, would see themselves psychologically significantly more external on locus of control. This first prediction was forecast on the basis of previous investigations of locus of control conducted with other deviant and drug user populations.

The first prediction was confirmed. Table 1 presents these results on locus of control for both the 1970 and 1990 samples.

TABLE 1		
Means and Standard Deviations of Locus of Control for First and Recidivist Drug Users, 1970 and 1990 Sample		
GROUP	MEANS	S.D.
1. First Offender (1970)	8.70	1.23
2. First Offender (1990)	9.01	1.20
3. Recidivist (1970)	10.08	1.64
4. Recidivist (1990)	11.30	1.44

Confirmation of this prediction established that CRC recidivist subjects for both the 1970 and 1990 samples did show significantly more externality than first time drug offenders. Further, this confirmation served to strengthen the relationship between externality and recidivism pointed out in prior studies of deviant populations (3). These results indicate that the 1990 sample rated themselves as more external than the 1970 sample. This finding was true for both the first and recidivist drug user samples. It would be interesting to conjecture why these two samples, separated by twenty years, demonstrate such a difference on locus of control and why the 1990 sample was more external on locus of control.

One possible explanation pertains to the users drug of choice. The majority of the 1970 sample admitted to heroin as their preferred substance. Cocaine and its derivative "crack" was used more frequently by the 1990 sample. Whereas heroin affects the body as a central nervous system depressant, cocaine is a stimulant. Many cocaine abusers admit to being physically and psychologically "out of control" when they ingest cocaine. It seems to logically follow that those users who use cocaine are more external than users who rely on a "downer"-type substance like heroin. Moreover, the majority of drug users admit to using marijuana as a first drug of choice. This study is in agreement with other research suggesting that marijuana is a gateway substance leading to use of "hard drugs". This relationship is detailed in Chapter IV - Marijuana As A Gateway Drug.

Several investigators have previously established that juvenile delinquents (4) and prisoners (5)(6) rely on external locus of control personality systems. Many psychologists have demonstrated that deviants, including drug users, tend to project or rationalize their life plight, attributing the causes for their deviance or addiction to other persons or environmental circumstances; very seldom to themselves. Laskowitz (7), who also investigated the psychological characteristics of the drug user, noted that drug users are susceptible to external forces because the user requires as much outside stimulus information about himself as possible. Lindesmith (8), in concert with Laskowitz, reported a similar need for external stimulation by drug users. Lindesmith contended that at an early point in the drug user's career he abdicates any hope of self determination in favor of a life governed by luck, fate, or chance occurrences. This perspective was very characteristic of the CRC drug user population, especially the cocaine addicted.

During personal interviews with select CRC users it was clear that recidivist users believed strongly that their lives were being controlled by outside forces. Those CRC drug offenders who felt controlled or "external" endorsed these statements from the locus of control scale:

- Children get into trouble because their parents punish them too much.

- Many of the unhappy things in people's lives are partly due to bad luck.

- Unfortunately, an individual's work often passes unrecognized no matter how hard he tries.

- Most students don't realize the extent to which their grades are influenced by accidental happenings.

- It is usually best to cover up one's mistakes.

- Without the right breaks one cannot be an effective leader.

- No matter how hard you try some people just don't like you.

- Getting a good job depends mainly on being in the right place at the right time.

- Many times we might just as well decide what to do by flipping a coin.

- Many times I feel that I have little influence over the things that happen to me.

The complete Locus of Control Scale with scoring instructions is presented in Appendix I. It might prove of interest for you to fill out the locus of control scale and determine whether or not you perceive that you are in control!

II. Older Versus Younger Drug Users - Locus of Control Position

The second prediction made in this study stated that older (27-35 years) CRC drug abusers will show significantly more externality than younger subjects (18-26 years). These results also confirmed this prediction. In fact, both the older 1970 and 1990 drug user samples showed more externality when compared with younger users. Table 2 presents the means and standard deviations on locus of control for older versus younger drug users.

TABLE 2		
Means and Standard Deviations of Locus of Control for Older (27-35 years) and Younger Drug Users 1970 and 1990 Samples		
GROUP	MEANS	S.D.
1. Older (1970)	11.43	1.40
2. Older (1990)	12.63	1.96
3. Younger (1970)	9.14	1.37
4. Younger (1990)	10.04	1.44

Confirmation may indicate that locus of control is not a persistent personality component and that over time it may shift. For example, Rotter has maintained that locus of control is an enduring, but not immutable personality construct, although he has not conducted investigations to test his assumptions. The results of this study do offer some support for Rotter's contention that locus of control change is possible and the change may be a function of aging. Unfortunately, the trend shows that externality is directly related to the age of the drug user. The results in Table 2 show that the 1990 sample, of both the older and younger drug users, were more external than the 1970 sample. A full discussion of the implications of these findings are included in Chapter V, Some Final Thoughts.

If the locus of control dimension does remain constant over time, then attempts to alter an external psychological orientation of a drug user may prove a more difficult undertaking. Furthermore, in light of these findings psychologists should not anticipate appreciable locus of control shifts among institutionalized drug users. It follows then that external individuals may be faced with their somewhat pessimistic orientations. This does not mean that institutional and outpatient therapy would have a negative impact. However, in the case of the external drug offender, active concern should be given to a direct therapeutic approach, such as reality or confrontational therapy. This outside strategy could be employed inside the institution as well as outside after release on parole.

The use of a direct counseling approach might serve the function of supplying external controls and focusing all the responsibility on the individual, especially for external individuals.

These findings regarding age and locus of control lend support to a number of previous investigations (9)(10), which likewise indicate older drug users demonstrate more psychological pathology than younger users.

It is well understood that most rehabilitation efforts with recidivist drug offenders have patently failed (11). Thus, psychologists and correctional workers alike must address themselves to the task of implementing new and more innovative therapy programs for drug users such as the ones used at CRC.

The treatment philosophy at CRC has always been toward a correctional concept first and there is little doubt that CRC has historically been oriented toward an enforcement model. This is readily apparent when one enters the institution through the barbed wire covered walls. However, many casual observers have severely castigated this institution along with its personnel. It has been my experience that CRC does a commendable job with the limited resources available. In a lengthy conversation with Associate Warden Grove, he explained that CRC is attempting to re-orient itself back to a more rehabilitative philosophy.

Because CRC is largely oriented around a "cottage plan", the institution lends itself to the development of a "controlled locus of control improvement program." Older offenders who reflect unfavorable external locus of control orientations might especially derive restorative personality benefits from such a program. In terms of release from CRC, it is reasonable to assume that measurable locus of control improvement while in therapy is one valid criterion to be considered prior to a resident's departure.

III. Locus of Control - Social Class Position

A third prediction that social economic class position is related to locus of control was measured. This study also attempted to relate ethnicity background to the locus of control variable. Three equal groups of Mexican-Americans, Blacks and Whites were sampled on the locus of control variable. Each group, randomly selected, was equal to eight CRC residents.

Prior research has demonstrated that both socio-economic status position and ethnicity are confounding factors in relation to assessment of locus of control. For that reason, the samples in this study were matched with respect to both socio-economic status and ethnic background. Frequency tables based upon social economic status and ethnic background are presented in Tables 3 and 4.

Table 3						
Comparison of Socio-Economic Status Between First and Recividist and Younger and Older Drug Users, 1970 Sample						
Warner Class Category	First Drug Offender	Recividist Drug Offender	Total	Younger Drug Offender	Older Drug Offender	Total
I. Upper & Upper Middle	1	0	1	1	2	3
II. Lower Middle	3	3	6	2	2	4
III. Upper Lower	16	18	34	19	18	37
IV. Lower Lower	4	3	7	2	2	4
Means	57.51	62.39		57.33	60.18	
S.D.	7.24	5.54		7.18	6.36	
N =	N = 24	N = 24	N = 48	N = 24	N = 34	N = 48

Table 4						
Comparison of Socio-Economic Status Between First and Recividist and Younger and Older Drug Users, 1990 Sample						
Warner Class Category	First Drug Offender	Recividist Drug Offender	Total	Younger Drug Offender	Older Drug Offender	Total
I. Upper & Upper Middle	1	2	3	1	2	4
II. Lower Middle	2	3	5	2	2	7
III. Upper Lower	2	2	4	5	10	9
IV. Lower Lower	19	17	36	16	12	28
Means	58.67	61.65		56.44	63.47	
S.D.	6.84	7.43		6.43	6.41	
N=	N=24	N=24	N=48	N=24	N=34	N=48

The results from Warner's Index of Status Characteristics, ISC, for socio-economic status were tabulated
and categorized for both the 1970 and 1990 samples. It
is evident that the majority of both first and recidivist
residents and younger older residents came from
Warner's Class IV (Upper-Lower)and Class V (Lower-
Lower). Thus, all the CRC subjects in this study came
preponderantly from a lower socio-economic strata. Because a homogeneity existed on ISC evaluations, the
writer assumed the differences found between the
samples on locus of control would not be attributable to
divergent social-economic identifications.

Three t-tests for mean differences were run for all
ethnic combinations for locus of control for both the 1970
and 1990 samples. While two of the three t-tests run
between the 1970 samples on locus of control were significant at the .01 level, e.g., Whites/Mexican-Americans
and Blacks/Whites, the t-tests between Mexican-
Americans and Blacks were significant at the .05 level.
The results of the 1990 samples were all significant at the
.05 level. These results are presented in Table 5.

Table 5		
t-tests for Locus of Control Among the Three Ethnic Groups		
Groups	t- test Values(1970)	t-test Values(1990)
Whites-Mexican Americans	-3.67*	-3.79**
Mexican-Americans Blacks	-2.24**	-3.67**
Whites - Black	-4.79*	-3.54**
* .01 level of significance		
**.05 level of significance		

Three t-tests for mean differences were also run for all ethnic combinations for self-concept for both the 1970 and 1990 samples. The results are presented in Table 6. The results of the 1970 self-concept sample indicate three levels of significance: Whites/Mexican-Americans were not significantly different; Mexican-Americans/Blacks were significant at the .05 level; and Black/Whites were significant at the .01 level. All statistical comparisons made on the 1990 samples were significant, i.e., Whites/Mexican-Americans at the .05 level; Mexican-American-Blacks at the .05 level; and Blacks/Whites at the .01 level. These results are presented in Table 6.

Table 6		
t-tests for Self-Concept Among the Three Ethnic Groups		
Groups	t- test Values(1970)	t-test Values(1990)
Whites-Mexican Americans	- .42*NS	-2.46**
Mexican-Americans Blacks	-2.65**	-2.74**
Whites - Black	-2.68*	-2.87**
* .01 level of significance		
**.05 level of significance		
NS = Not Significant		

Table 7 presents the means and standard deviations on self-concept for the three ethnic groups.

Table 7				
Means and Standard Deviations on Locus of Control for three Ethnic Groups of Drug Users				
		White	Mexican-American	Black
I- E (1970)	Means	7.14	9.72	11.31
	SD	1.60	1.61	2.41
I-E (1990)	Means	8.72	10.72	13.01
	SD	1.54	9.10	3.69

IV. First Versus Experienced Drug Users - Self-Concept Position

The fourth prediction stated that recidivists, or experienced users, when compared with a matched sample of first offender subjects, would rate themselves significantly less favorably on self-concept than first offenders. The basis for this prediction is derived from prior self-concept investigations involving deviants and drug users that indicated that recidivist samples have less favorable self-concepts than first offenders. It seemed logical to predict that recidivist drug offenders would have more depreciated self-concepts than first drug offenders.

These self-concept data concerning first and recidivist subjects are presented in Table 8.

TABLE 8		
Means and Standard Deviations on Measures of Self-Concept for RC First and Recidivist Drug Users		
Group (N-24)	Means	S. D.
1. First Offender (1970)	23.71	4.70
2. First Sample (1990)	26.35	4.33
3. Recidivist (1970)	27.41	4.12
4. Recidivist (1990)	28.68	4.56

V. Older Versus Younger Users - Self-Concept Position

The fifth prediction stated that older (27-35 years) CRC subjects for both first and recidivist status would report significantly less favorable self-concepts. The rationale for this prediction grew out of an investigation of older and younger institutionalized drug users conducted by Schiff. Schiff concluded that the older subjects in his sample reflected more behavior maladjustment including unfavorable self-concepts. Therefore, it seemed reasonable to test for self-concept differences among the CRC residents.

The means and standard deviations for the self-concept scores for CRC old and young subjects for 1970 and 1990 are presented in Table 9.

TABLE 9		
Means and Standard Deviations on Self-Concept for Younger and Older Drug Users		
Group(N = 24)	Means	S. D
1. Young (1970)	27.31	4.24
2. Young (1990)	26.54	4.31
3. Older (1970)	27.48	4.61
4. Older (1990)	29.72	4.71

From the standpoint of rehabilitation and prevention of drug abuse, it is simply impractical, and perhaps as Duster (12) suggested, even immoral to cast all drug offenders into the same program and hope that effective treatment will be brought about. Duster conducted one of the first in depth studies of CRC. In the final analysis such treatment involves little more than detoxification and custody. Rarely, if ever, are incoming drug users at CRC properly differentiated with regard to various personality dimensions. Usually, the therapeutic goal there is to terminate drug ingestion and the success of the treatment is measured in terms of detoxification and "clean time" and not as an assessment of psychological adjustment or personality modification.

VI. Self-Concept - Social Class/Position

A sixth prediction that social economic position is related to self-concept was examined here. An analysis of self-concept was also related to social class position. Three equal groups of Blacks, Mexican-American and Whites were measured on self-concept. The research samples were matched with respect to both socio-economic position and ethnicity. Complete frequency tables based on socio-economic class are presented in Tables 4 and 5.

The results from Warner's ISC were tabulated and categorized for both the 1970 and 1990 samples. It is evident that the majority of both first and recidivist and younger older residents came from Warner's Class IV and V. All the CRC subjects in this study came preponderantly from a lower socio-economic strata. Because a homogeneity existed on ISC evaluation, the writer assumed the differences found between the samples on locus of control would not be attributable to divergent socio-economic identifications.

Similar to the locus of control results, three t-tests were run for all ethnic combinations for self-concept. While two of the three t-tests (1970) run between the ethnic groups on self-concept were significant at the .01 level (Whites-Mexican American and Blacks-Whites) the t-test between Blacks and Mexican-Americans was significant at the .05 level. The results of the 1990 sample indicate that all group differences were at the .05 level of significance. These results are presented in Table 10.

TABLE 10		
t-test for Self-Concept Among the Three Ethnic Groups		
Groups	t-test Values(1970)	t-test Values(1990)
Whites-Mexican Americans	-3.48*	-3.86
Mexican-Americans Blacks	-3.42**	-4.24**
Blacks - Whites	-3.87	-3.87 *
*.01 level of significance		
** .05 level of significance		

Table 11 presents the means and standard deviations on self-concept for the three ethnic groups.

TABLE 11				
Means and Standard Deviations on Self-Concept for Three Ethnic Groups of Drug Users				
		White	Mexican-American	Black
Self-Concept (1970)	Means	8.18	9.781	2.44
	SD	1.70	1.73	1.87
Self-Concept (1990)	Means	8.64	11.40	13.94
	SD	1.72	4.73	4.07

As a group, the White samples for both the 1970 and 1990, in comparison with the Mexican-American sample, showed significant differences on self-concept assessments. While the White sample tended toward more positive self-concept formation, the Mexican-American sample showed lower self-concepts. This finding was true for both the 1970 and 1990 results.

In contrast, the Mexican-American sample, in comparison with the Black sample, showed significant differences on self-concept assessment, e.g. Mexican-Americans reported more favorable self-concept assessments.

Significant differences were found also between the White and the Black samples on self-concept with the former group demonstrating more favorable self-concept formation. For both the 1970 and 1990 samples the Black sample rated themselves more negative on self-concept.

VII. Locus of Control and Self-Concept - The Relationship

Prediction VII stated that locus of control and self-concept are significantly and positively related: internality is positively correlated with favorable self-concept. The basis of this hypothesis developed from prior investigations which showed a positive relationship between locus of control and self-concept. Two studies in particular have proved that internality is positively related to favorable self-concept assessment and vice-versa(13),(14).

The Pearson product-moment of $r = .504$ for 1970 and $r = .674$ for 1990 confirmed the relationship between internality and favorable self-concept. Table 12 gives the means, standard deviations and coefficient between the locus of and self-concept scores for the whole CRC sample.

TABLE 12			
Means, Standard Deviations and Product Moment Correlation Between Locus of Control and Self-Concept Scores for the Whole CRC Population, 1970 - 1990			
Group			
Internal-External Locus of Control Scores		Self-Concept Scores	
1970	1990	1970	1990
Mean 9.30	Mean 9.50	Mean 25.00	Mean 24.40
S.D. 1.64	S.D. 1.54	S.D. 4.66	S.D. 4.41
r = .504 (1970)		r = .674 (1990)	

MARIJUANA AS A GATEWAY DRUG

During the CRC research studies the total sample was asked which drug of choice they initially used. These results clearly indicate that marijuana was the first drug of choice, leading later to the use of more harmful substances. A series of past research interviews also confirmed this use of marijuana as a first drug leading to other "hard drugs." These CRC results are convincing in the support of the assertion that marijuana is, in fact, a gateway substance.

During the research phase the sample (N = 48) was presented with a background questionnaire. This questionnaire was designed to collect demographic background data on the sample. The complete background data is presented in Chapter II. Tables 6-9 show the background information and presents seven categories of data: 1) mean age, 2) mean educational level, 3) marital status, 4) religious preference, 5) mean time of drug use, 6) time of prior institutionalization, and 7) first drug used.

Tables 13-17 presents a tabulation of the responses to category 7: First Drug used.

Table 17 shows a summary of all categories of drugs selected as first drug used.

Table 13			
First Drug Used			
CRC First Offenders (1970)			
Age 18-26			
	White	Mexican-American	Black	Total
Cocaine	3	1	1	5
Marijuana	10	12	13	35
Speed	2	2	1	5
Hallucinogen				
Opiate				
Other	1		1	2
Not Reporting		1		1

141

Table 14			
First Drug Used			
CRC First Offenders (1970)			
Age 27-35			
	White	Mexican-American	Black	Total
Cocaine	2	1	2	5
Marijuana	12	13	14	39
Speed	2	2		4
Hallucinogen				
Opiate				
Other				
Not Reporting				

Table 15			
First Drug Used			
CRC First Offenders (1990)			
Age 18-26			
	White	Mexican-American	Black	Total
Cocaine	1	1	2	4
Marijuana	14	13	14	41
Speed	1	2		3
Hallucinogen				
Opiate				
Other				
Not Reporting		1		1

Table 16

First Drug Used

CRC First Offenders (1990)

Age 27-35

	White	Mexican-American	Black	Total
Cocaine	1	1	1	3
Marijuana	14	13	15	42
Speed		2		2
Hallucinogen				
Opiate				
Other	1			1
Not Reporting		1		1

Table 17	
Summary of	
First Drug Used	
	Total
Cocaine	16
Marijuana	157
Speed	14
Hallucinogen,	
Opiate,	
Other	3
Not Reporting	3
Total Reporting	193

The percentage of all users sampled reporting marijuana as the first drug of choice was equal to 81% of the first drug used. The second catagory, cocaine, only accounts for 8% of the first drug used. Based on these results, in this writer's view, there is little doubt that marijuana does lead to the use of more harmful substances.

CHAPTER IV

REFERENCES

1.NATIONAL DRUG CONTROL STRATEGY, U. S. Government Printing Office, 1989, P. 25 and 38.

2.NATIONAL DRUG CONTROL STRATEGY, U.S. Government Printing Office, 1989, P. 38.

3.LEFCOURT, H. M. and LADWIG, G. W. "The American Negro; a problem in expectancies". *J. Pers. Soc. Psychol.*, 1965, 1,pp 377, 380.

4.RICHARD, W. C., MATES, C. G., and WHITTEN, L. "Personality traits and attitudes of adolescent girls with behavior disorders". Unpublished paper, presented at Southeastern Psychol. Associat., 1967.

5.LADWIG, G. W. "Personal, situational and social determinants of preference for delayed reinforcement".Unpublished doctoral dissertation, Ohio State University,1963.

6.SEEMAN, M. "Social learning theory and the theory of mass society". Unpublished paper presented at the American Social. Society, 1963.

7.LASKOWITZ, D. "Psychological characteristics of the adolescent addict". In *Harms, E.* (ed.). " Drug addiction in youth". *Oxford: Pergamon Press*, 1965.

8.LINDESMITH, A. "Addiction and opiates". Chicago: *Aldine Publishing Company*, 1968.

9.HURLEY, W. H. "A study of the self-concepts of criminals and non-criminals". Unpublished doctoral dissertation, The University of Oklahoma, 1961.

10.CHEIN, L. GERARD, D. C., LEE, R. S., and ROSEN-FELD, E. *The road to H.* New York: Basic Books, 1964.

11.DUVALL, H. J., LOCKE, B. Z. and BRILL, L. Follow-up study of narcotic drug addicts five years after hospitalization.

12.DUSTER, T. *The Legislation of Morality*, Toronto, Canada. The Free Press, 1970.

13.FRANKLIN, R. D. "Youth's expectancies about internal versus external control of reinforcement related to N variables". Unpublished doctoral dissertation. Purdue University, 1963.

14.RICHARD, W. C., MATES, C. G., and WHITTEN, L. "Personality traits and attitudes of adolescent girls with behavior disorders". Unpublished paper, presented at Southeastern Psychol. Associat., 1967.

CHAPTER V

SOME FINAL THOUGHTS

SUMMARY POSITION

Today's Epidemic

Today, the problem of drug abuse assumes epidemic proportions internationally, and domestically it covers the entire strata of U.S. society. In fact, drug abuse may be more widespread in 1990 than it was in 1970. In 1970, when the writer embarked on the original CRC research project, the news media labeled the U. S. drug crisis as being "out of control." Today, in 1990, the same phrase is applicable. The number of persons under thirty years of age found to be addicted to a wide variety of drugs is constantly increasing. More than twelve percent of the American workforce admits to using drugs. There has been a dramatic increase frequency and percentage of people arrested who were found to be addicted. Table 1 data from the National Institute of Justice shows these percentages (1).

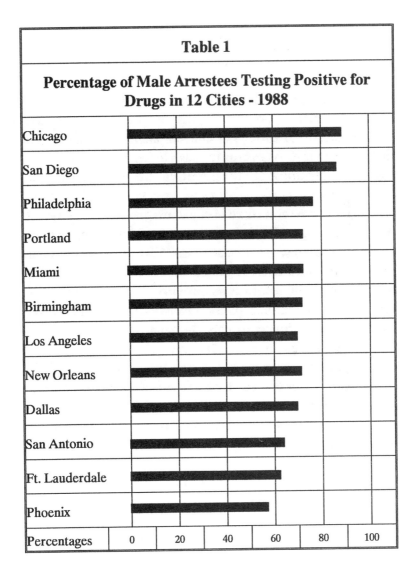

Table 1
Percentage of Male Arrestees Testing Positive for Drugs in 12 Cities - 1988

With this high rate of chemical dependency, it is no wonder that U.S. labor is losing out to more abstinent Asian countries. "Crack" and the synthetic metham-phetamine derivative, "ice," may be the most addictive substance ever known! The current crack trial of Marion Barry, Mayor of Washington, D.C., bears evidence that no one is immune from the negative effects of drug abuse.

The youthful nature of the drug problem is reflected by the disproportionate representation of younger drug offenders in institutions such as CRC. To worsen an already bad situation it seems that treatment measures available to drug users have patently failed. As a result, the recidivism rate reported by some drug treatment experts has soared as high as 94 percent.

California may be particularly hard hit by the increase in drug abuse. In a 1990 State Assembly study on self-esteem, the chair of the study, Mr. Vasconcellos directed his committee's attention to the state's chemical dependency problem (2). Consider these findings:

- Approximately 2.1 million persons in California use illicit drugs or misuse legal drugs.

- In California, 222,000 people use drugs in-travenously, increasing the risk of spreading AIDS.

152

- An estimated 3 million Americans are addicted to cocaine.

- An estimated 10 percent of those who have ever used cocaine become addicts, and they consume 75 percent of the cocaine used in the United States.

- Perhaps 450,000 Californians are addicted to cocaine, many to the highly addictive smokable form called crack.

- Almost two out of three persons arrested for any felony in Los Angeles tested positive for cocaine. Arrestees often test positive for multiple (poly) drug use, including combinations with alcohol.

- In California, a 1985 study concluded that almost half of the persons in prison had been under the influence of alcohol at the time the criminal offense was committed.

- Heroin addicts are estimated to engage in criminal activities for about half the days in a year.

- Over three out of every four persons arrested for a felony in San Diego and Los Angeles recently tested positive for an illegal drug other than marijuana.

- In 1989, for the first time in California's history, felony drug arrests became the single largest crime category, surpassing property arrests.

A search for an explanation to determine which individuals are predisposed to drug use, in addition to implementation of new and innovative treatment methods and the development of effective controls, have so far evaded even the most sophisticated authorities in law enforcement, medicine and the social sciences. The federal government's tangle of drug enforcement agencies has proved confusing to everyone, especially the government itself! The federal drug czar, William Bennett, has spent most of his time dealing with bureaucracy and precious little time dealing with actual drug offenders. Dr. Bennett has stated that even Washington has a limited role: "There are things the federal government can't do. Restore the moral authority of families, churches, and schools, and you get rid of 85% of this problem." (3) One fact is clear - the government's law enforcement policy has failed to curb the U.S. drug dilemma (4).

The government's costs associated with drug treatment is staggering. A 1987 report conducted by the National Institute in Drug Abuse (Table 2) shows these expenditures divided into private, federal and state/local economies (5).

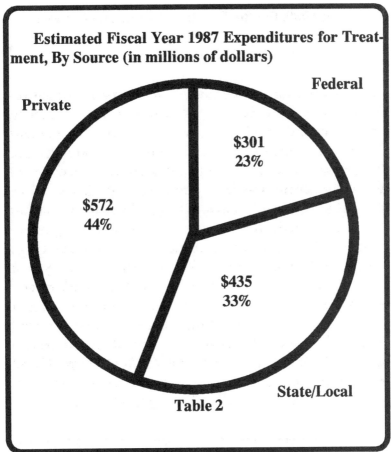

Estimated Fiscal Year 1987 Expenditures for Treatment, By Source (in millions of dollars)

Federal

Private

$301
23%

$572
44%

$435
33%

State/Local

Table 2

In another study, it appears that the U. S. consumption of drugs is increasing. However, more young people realize that the use of illegal drugs, especially cocaine, is dangerous. In 1988, the National Institute on Drug Abuse released the results of a nationwide high school survey (6). These results are reported in Table 3.

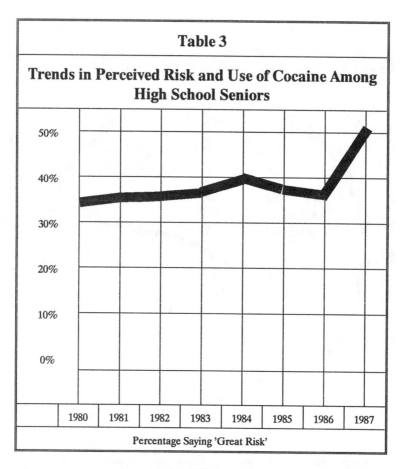

Table 3

Trends in Perceived Risk and Use of Cocaine Among High School Seniors

Percentage Saying 'Great Risk'

It is quite apparent the **1987** sample perceived cocaine to be more dangerous than did their **1980-86** counterparts.

156

This writer contends that at least three special areas of drug research warrant our careful attention: 1) the laws regulating drug use and traffic and the criminal sanctions meted out to the drug user; 2) the treatment procedures for the drug user; and 3) the psychodynamics of the drug user. The last two areas were specifically treated at length in the present investigation.

Psychologically, the interpretations of drug use are multiple, although it is accepted that the drug user presents a clinical picture characterized by emotional immaturity, orientation to the present and behavior maladjustment. Research studies have established that typical drug users often reveal depreciated self-regard and in their recourse to rationalizations for having become addicted, they tend to project the reasons for their plight outside themselves.

The concern of this investigation developed more than 20 years ago out of a sense of need to better understand the psychodynamics of the first-time and recidivist drug users, older versus younger users, and to be able to differentiate between drug users on the basis of psychological personality correlates.

Today we still know very little about treatment outcome of one drug program versus another. This was especially the case in 1970. Recently, however, research

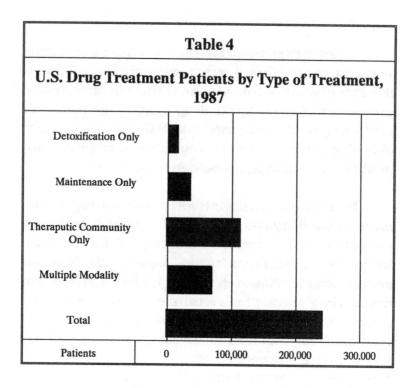

Table 4

U.S. Drug Treatment Patients by Type of Treatment, 1987

supports the belief that the type of treatment modality, as well as the length of stay is related to positive outcome. The following gives a rough breakdown of the type of treatment provided to U. S. patients during 1987 and this information is presented in Table 4 (7).

If we are able to combine this type of treatment information with the personality results of this study, we have taken a big step in terms of relating the type of treatment to the specific abuser.

158

Many psychologists have called for a comprehensive assessment of the psychological factors related to drug use in order to differentiate users from other deviant groups as well as the other groups from each other. This study was undertaken to assess two psychological variables, locus of control and self-concept among a group of institutionalized drug users committed at CRC.

Established in 1961 as the first state-operated treatment center specifically designed to handle the criminal drug abuser, CRC seemed an ideal facility to investigate the psychology of the drug user. Although thousands of drug users have been treated at CRC, only several detailed investigations of the institution have been undertaken. CRC was particularly amenable for study not only because it has gone unnoticed, but also because it has served as an exemplar for other states such as Illinois and New Jersey. More important perhaps, CRC has demonstrated an impressive success rate ranging as high as 35 percent for the first time releases reported in one follow-up study. Thus, after a twenty year interval, this writer went back to CRC in June of 1990 in order to gather new psychological data for the updated follow-up investigation.

Seven major predictions were made in both studies. In addition to the testing of these primary areas, a subsequent analysis was conducted in order to assess the effects of ethnicity, which was employed as a control variable on locus of control and self-concept. In the writer's view, the implications of this research have primary relevance in three areas:

1. These experimental findings can be applied toward development of differential therapeutic treatment programs while drug offenders are institutionalized.

2. This investigation suggests that changes in the locus of control and self-concept of drug offenders are important psychological variables which can be included as criteria for determination of offender release.

3. This research is germane for the determination of differential post-release practices for drug offenders after reinstatement in the community.

Each prediction is discussed in terms of these three areas.

As reported above in Chapter IV, predictions one and four interpreted together concern the effect of offender status on the locus of control and self-concept dimensions. It was confirmed that CRC recidivist subjects did show significantly more externality and had less favorable self-concepts than the first drug offenders committed at CRC. Further, confirmation of the first prediction served to strengthen the relationship between externality and recidivism pointed out in prior studies of deviant populations.

Additional investigators have established that juvenile delinquents (8) and prisoners (9), (10) rely on an external locus of control. Many criminological works suggested that deviants tend to project or rationalize their life plight, attributing the causes for their deviance to other persons or environmental circumstances. Sykes and Matza (11) formulated the concept "techniques of neutralization" to explain the reasoning in which juvenile delinquents engage to explain their behavior. Central to these "techniques of neutralization" is the systematic denial of responsibility or projection of the consequences of their actions. Thus, deviant behavior seen in terms of neutralization theory may be the result of such mitigating circumstances as bad companions, ghetto-dwelling, the police, etc. These factors tend to project the deviant causes away from the individual and toward outside influences. In a like manner, innumerable stories taken from heroin addicts (12) are pervaded with themes that project or deny personal responsibility.

Laskowitz (13), who investigated the psychological characteristics of drug users, noted that they are practically susceptible to external forces because the user requires as much stimulus information about himself as possible. Lindesmith (14) in concert with Laskowitz, reported a similar need for external stimulation by drug users. Lindesmith contended that at an early point in the drug user's career he/she abdicates any hope of self determination in favor of a life governed by luck, chance or fate occurrences. In keeping with these investigations it becomes evident that any form of treatment with the drug user must strive to develop responsible patterns of behavior in order to be effective.

Support for prediction four suggested that the process of self-concept deterioration among recidivist institutionalized drug users is similar to that reported in self-concept investigations among other recidivist groups (15).

The relationship between recidivism and self-concept is corroborated by the findings of other self-concept studies with deviants such as prisoners (16). The results of parallel investigations of first and recidivist offender status of juvenile delinquents conducted by Balester (17), and more recently by Lefeber (18), who carefully noted that recidivists are more maladjusted than first offenders, compare favorably with the results in this study. The high recidivism rate for drug offenders, together with the implications from this study, leads us to the point of reassessment of the validity of the therapeutic programs presently used with the drug addict. The writer submits that the failure of corrections' personnel to account for the differential personality characteristics of the inmates has led to the serious impairment of the accuracy of their parole predictions. It can be recommended that assessment of changes in locus of control during an inmate's imprisonment might yield valuable data pertaining to psychological adjustment. If a person begins to take responsibility for his actions, then reliance on drugs ought to decrease.

Ausubel (19) pointed out the benefit of embracing the psychological factors in order to explain drug use. He contended that "perhaps the most important of research tasks is the definitive identification through controlled longitudinal studies of the personality factors that predispose to addiction and affect prognosis of therapy."

If one assumes that two goals of successful therapy with drug users might include strengthening internal control and enhancement of self-concept, then psychotherapy with drug users should strive toward these ends. Furthermore, cognizant of these locus of control and self-concept differences between first and recidivist CRC offenders, it follows that the process of therapy with the two groups should also differ.

According to Bordin (20) and Patterson (21), one of the important bases for the delineation of systems of psychotherapy is whether the method is directive or non-directive. These writers have arranged the systems in accordance with a conceptual directive - non-directive continuum. At the extreme directive end of such continuum are those methods that encourage the therapist to openly confront the patient's world view, values, and beliefs. Both the tenets of reality therapy as espoused by Glasser (22) and confrontation therapy (23) typify this approach.

At the non-directive or permissive end would fall those therapies that stress a more passive-acceptant role for the therapist. Rogers' (24) client-oriented therapy, also labeled non-directive, is representative of this viewpoint. These treatment approaches are, of course, not mutually exclusive for they do share certain techniques in common; however, the former approach does tend to operate on the assumption that the therapist must provide active direction and orientation for the client, while implicit in the latter is client reliance and self-direction, goal setting and strength. These divergent philosophies of treatment are relevant for this discussion of locus of control and self-concept drug users.

The advantages of both approaches are manifold; however, it seems clear that we cannot expect that all individuals will profit equally from the same method.

On the basis of the locus of control and self-concept data in this study the writer proffers that a non-directive therapy such as the client-centered approach is most applicable for only certain kinds of drug addicts. First offenders who show a more internal locus of control and are favorable on self-concept and who accept responsibility for their behavior seem particularly amenable to this method.

Additionally, research on both locus of control (25) and self-concept (26) has shown a positive relationship between client insight and internality and favorable self-concept. In the light of these relationships and the findings in this study, it is plausible to argue that first offenders who are internal on locus of control and more favorable on self-concept and who show insight into their behavior would not require the imposed goal-setting, control, and confrontation methods basic to a direct approach such as reality therapy or confrontational-type therapy (27). These offenders who accept the responsibility and blameworthiness for their action require a therapeutic climate of supportive guidance best afforded by the non-directive approach.

In contrast, recidivist offenders, external on locus of control and unfavorable on self-concept, who fail to accept the responsibility for their behavior, might benefit from a direct therapy such as Glasser's reality therapy (28). While this type of confrontation therapy can be recommended for the recidivist offender; if used with first offenders it might produce a psychologically adverse or paradoxical effect. Glasser (29) noted that juvenile delinquents and prisoners are particularly resistant to non-directive approaches. Glasser formulated the system of reality therapy for juvenile delinquents, who, in his opinion, tend to exploit the tradition-supportive methods. Deeply embedded in this approach is the notion that the therapist must point out to the patient how he has become mentally ill or deviant through projection of personal responsibility: "People do not act irresponsibly because they are 'ill'; they are 'ill' because they act irresponsibly." Supportive therapy releases the patient or the delinquent from personal responsibility and, in Glasser's view, therapists are willing to accept the deviant's denials, projections and rationalizations: " We never agree that his (delinquent's) responsibility is justified no matter how much he may have suffered at the hands of others (30)."

It follows that the therapeutic goal for the reality therapist treating the drug user is identification of irresponsible behavior patterns and subsequent confrontation with such maladaptive responses to enable the individual to reclaim techniques of responsible adaptation. Additionally, the findings reported here are relevant with regard to maintenance or violation of parole status for drug users released from CRC or similar facilities. Re-admission rates for drug offenders released from many state and federal treatment centers approximate the 90 percent level.

One possible explanation to account for this high rate concerns which offenders are released from institutions, when they are subject to release, and what release criteria are used by the administration to determine release. Too often in prisons and drug treatment centers these critical decisions derive from nebulous information contained in the offender's institutional file.

Three of the variables thought by correctional officials to have the greatest discriminating power for a parole are the inmate's criminal history, the history of adjustment during incarceration, and the type of deviant career. Prediction tables employing these factors are often devised for the purpose of deciding who will be released. Much of this information does have merit. Unfortunately, the data accumulated in the inmate's file does not account for essential personality dynamics nor does it consider the modification of the inmate's personality during periods of confinement. Garrity, who examined the parole release procedures for a number of state prisons, comments on the utility of such files (31): " They do not contain detailed information concerning the primary associations of the prisoners, measures of his self-conception...or other factors."

Faced with the complex business of determining who shall be released, the treatment staff at a large institution like CRC makes its decision largely upon the same kind of data used by the adult parole board. At CRC the primary indicators for release rest on the staff's subjective impression of the inmate's therapeutic progress, the existence of an outside occupation and a group of reliable acquaintances who must not be users. Duster pointed out that:

> The treatment staff makes a judgment as to when the resident is ready to leave the Rehabilitation Center and return to the community. As has been indicated, there is no clear set of actions that are known to be the pathway out of the institution. One critical factor that is commonly acknowledged is the readiness of the community to which the addict is returning to provide a place for him that maximizes a drug-free life. The primary indicators of this for the staff seem to be (1) the existence of an occupation and (2) the newness of surroundings and the nature of acquaintances. It is especially important that the acquaintances are not users. The treatment staff makes a decision to release the resident based largely upon their imputation of what the receiving community is like. This means that the staff must have some conception of what a good community is, and this conception will greatly influence its judgment of who is ready to leave the institution. The staff-inmate split, as we have seen in another context, coincides with a social-class split.(32)

The writer submits that the failure of corrections personnel to account for the differential personality characteristics of the drug user inmate has led to the serious impairment of the accuracy of their parole predictions. It can be recommended that assessment of changes in locus of control and self-concept during a person's imprisonment might yield valuable data pertaining to psychological adjustment. The findings from this study are also germane to post-release practices with drug offenders.

The California program for civil commitment at CRC is divided into the CRC resident phase and an outpatient post-release phase. Once a resident is eligible for release from CRC there are basically two outpatient parole plans which may be applicable. One, the halfway house program, to which the releasee is sent, provides intensive short-term group therapy for about fifty individuals who are closely supervised. More importantly, this milieu, which establishes a modicum of control and guidance by parole officers and counselors, is a powerful, structured therapeutic setting and must be considered for externally-controlled recidivist offenders who reflect low self-concepts. It can help these individuals, who need external support and control, to realize that the halfway house setting is only a theoretical halfway distance between CRC and normal community life.

The casework plan, the other option for release to outpatient status, which involves less parole supervision or surveillance, is recommended for the first-time offender internally controlled and showing a favorable self-concept. This arrangement is more informal and less demanding in comparison to the halfway house plan. The caseworker, who meets weekly with the releasee at his home, can provide supportive, humanistic therapy, as well as group, family or marital counseling. The goal of this program is to facilitate the releasee's adjustment during the critical first phase of transition back to the community.

Prediction two in this study, proposing that older CRC subjects would demonstrate significantly more externality than the younger subjects, was also confirmed. Confirmation of this prediction may indicate that locus of control does not remain a consistent personality component. For example, Rotter (33) has for some time maintained that locus of control is an enduring, immutable construct, although he has not conducted empirical investigations to test his hypothesis. The results of this study do not support Rotter's contention.

If the locus of control dimension remains constant over time, then attempts to alter an external orientation may prove a more difficult undertaking than affecting positive modification of the self-concept. Furthermore, in light of these findings psychologists should not anticipate radical locus of control shifts among drug users who are involved in treatment programs. It follows that external individuals are faced with their consistent locus of control orientations. This does not mean that institutional and outpatient therapy would have negative impact. However, in the case of the external offender, active concern should be given to a direct therapeutic approach, such as reality therapy. This could be employed inside the institution as well as after release. The use of a direct approach might serve the function of supplying external controls and focusing all the responsibility on the individual.   Another interpretation of this finding relates to the psychology of drug addiction. The psychodynamics of drug use are of such a mixed pathology as suggested by Ausubel (34), that perhaps any attempt to differentiate users on the basis of a unitary relationship between locus of control and age is apt to attribute too little attention to the larger constellation of factors bound-up with drug use. Whereas, the relation between locus of control and age studied alone may not be a sensitive index for accurate differentiation between CRC first and recidivist offenders, in combination with other psychological variables, age may well prove more explanatory.

Other data concerning the younger and older CRC subjects was collected from the research questionnaire used in this study. For example, the results indicated that there are differences for older and younger offenders with regard to their history of drug use and drug patterning. While many of the older subjects reported the use of opiates as their first drug, this was reported by only seven of the younger subjects. Additionally, many more of the 1990 sample used cocaine and "crack" the latter drug not available to the 1970 group. Additional biographical data suggested that the two age groups also differed in that the younger subjects report histories pervaded by the ingestion of the soft drugs, then a later shift to opiate-type drugs, whereas the older residents reported a longer history of opiate-type drug consumption.

These findings regarding age may lend support to a number of prior investigations (35), (36), which likewise indicate older users demonstrate more psychological pathology than younger users. Predictions that older CRC residents (27-35 years) in both first and recidivist offender status were significantly less favorable on measures of self-concept than younger residents (18-26 years). This finding demonstrated that there are personality differences between older and younger drug users in terms of self-concept evaluation. This finding may contribute to a better understanding of the different psychological characteristics of younger and older drug users.

Also, this evidence substantiated the results of previous self-concept investigations with other deviant groups (37), which indicated that offender age affects self-concept. For instance, Hurley examined the extent to which age influences the self-concept of prisoners confined to a Texas prison. Half of the inmates in that study were older offenders (27 years old and older) and the other half were younger offenders (19 years old and under). Hurley concluded that the older offenders were significantly less favorable on self-concept than the younger offenders. The results of this study demonstrated a similar finding.

The implications from this relationship has meaning for differential forms of institutional therapy with drug users. It was pointed out that one optimal goal in psychotherapy might be self-concept improvement. Psychologists, in their attempt to evaluate progress in psychotherapy, have maintained that self-concept improvement is one demonstrable measure of therapeutic success (38). Investigation of therapy outcome in psychiatric hospitals and counseling centers has revealed that during and after therapy there is an increase in patient self acceptance and a decrease in both self-condemnation and negativistic attitudes toward the self (39), (40). In a criminological investigation of the effect of therapy, Cole (41) measured post-therapy self-concept improvement for a group of thirty-eight institutionalized juvenile delinquents. Cole theorized that an unfavorable self-concept figures largely into the psychodynamics of delinquent patterns; thus, facilitation of a healthy self-concept quite possibly serve to deter delinquent behavior.

In an effort to test this hypothesis Cole developed a differential reinforcement treatment program aimed at improving self-concept. The results of a pre-post test condition showed, as predicted, that delinquents involved in the program did show enhancement of self-concept compared with a group of non-therapy controls.

Implications from the results of the above described Cole study lend themselves to the present study, with the indication that a similar self-concept improvement program could be beneficial for institutionalized drug users, such as those committed to CRC. The future development of such a program is certainly one direction therapy could take with the drug addict.

It is well understood that rehabilitation efforts with recidivist drug offenders have patently failed (42). Thus, psychologists and correctional workers must address themselves to the task of implementing new and innovative therapy programs such as the Cole model. Because CRC is oriented around the cottage plan, the institution lends itself to the development of a controlled self-concept improvement program. Older offenders who reflect unfavorable self-concepts might especially derive restorative personality benefits from such a program. In terms of release from CRC, it is reasonable to assume that self-concept improvement while in therapy is a valid criterion to be considered prior to a resident's departure.

If a CRC resident engaged in a program of self-concept therapy shows favorable improvement and is subsequently released, this should not mean that such therapy should terminate. In fact, it is sound to reason that the post-release phase of treatment programs like California's should include an intensive self-concept program for releasees. The outpatient therapy, conducted either individually or in groups, should be conducted by a psychologist or psychologically trained parole agent. Only by the creation of such therapy programs, both inside and outside the institution, can we come to terms with the difficult task of rehabilitation of the drug offender.

Prediction seven was also confirmed. It stated that locus of control and self-concept are significantly and positively correlated; internality is positively correlated with favorable self-concept. These results confirm this for both the 1970 and 1990 samples. This finding revealed that CRC residents who showed high internality reflected concomitant favorable self-concepts; conversely, residents with high externality reflected unfavorable self-concepts.

Fitts and Hamner (43) have established that favorable self-concept and internality are positively related for female prisoners. This relationship indicated that subjects with positive and healthy self-concepts typically display an internal locus of control. In contrast, subjects with poor self-concepts tend to have an external locus of control. Fitts and Hamner's results serve to corroborate the findings of an earlier study by Richard (44), who found a direct and positive correction between favorable self-concept and internality among female delinquents. The findings of these two investigations provide encouraging, although not completely unambiguous support for the present study. Because this study dealt with a population of male drug users, it must be noted that the two studies described above dealt with female prisoners; thus, there are certain predictable differences between the groups as a function of the offender's sex. Besides the Fitts and Hamner and Richard investigations and additional work which is tangentially relevant, there are no definitive studies which correlate locus of control and self-concept of drug users.

Psychological investigators such as Freedman (45) and Ausubel (46), have called for further exploration into the personality dynamics of drug users in order to formulate an explanatory typology of the drug user. As research studies confirmed, the positive relationship between locus of control and self-concept and offers the potential for development of such typology. Furthermore, confirmation of this hypothesis is pertinent for determination of which drug users should be treated at CRC. It was suggested that the re-admission rate for drug offenders released from many state and federal institutions approximates the 90 percent level. One possible explanation for this high rate of failure concerns the amenability of a specific treatment program for the individual user.

It can be reasoned from these results relating locus of control and self-concept, that drug offenders who rely on external locus of control and reflect unfavorable self-concepts are not particularly suited for either the treatment philosophy or the therapeutic methods presently available at CRC. In other words, while CRC might be effective with one type of drug offender, it might be equally ineffective with another. Therefore, it logically follows that a number of CRC residents who violate the conditions of parole on release should not have been sent to CRC. If, for example, on the basis of precommitment screening, it is determined from locus of control, self-concept and other sensitive psychodiagnostic instruments that a particular drug offender is external and reflects an unfavorable self-concept, then immediate referral is indicated. Such an offender would benefit from other programs. For instance, confrontational therapy, which stresses self-help and Glasser's reality therapy has demonstrated success among recidivist drug users. Unfortunately, large state-supported programs like CRC have little choice but to accept all court-committed persons, except those with deviant felony records marked by profoundly aggravated criminal activity. In California, the law excludes from CRC commitment only specific narcotics crimes and certain violent offenders (47).

From the standpoint of rehabilitation and prevention of drug abuse, it is simply impractical, and perhaps as Duster (48) suggested, even immoral, to cast all drug offenders into the same program and hope that effective treatment will be brought about. In the final analysis such treatment involves little more than detoxification and custody. Rarely, if ever, are incoming drug users at CRC properly differentiated with regard to various personality dimensions. Usually, the therapeutic goal there is to terminate drug ingestion and the success of the treatment is measured in terms of detoxification and "clean time" and not as as assessment of psychological adjustment or personality modification.

Confirmed research pertaining to the relationship between locus of control and self-concept is far from complete, but impressive beginnings are being made concerning various deviant groups such as juvenile delinquents, prisoners, and now including the institutionalized drug user. The results of the present study serve to corroborate the prior work reported here. Despite these rich beginnings, it is apparent that more studies among drug users are needed before we can positively differentiate among drug users. Perhaps one of the main shortcomings of this previous research is the use of different research populations. Obviously, there is the difficulty of comparing the results from female subjects with those from male subjects; and there is the problem presented by using different research instruments, particularly in the case of self-concept assessment.

A further exploration of locus of control and self-concept data produced the following analysis. The results of the t-tests run between the ethnic groups point out significant differences on both locus of control and self-concept among the three ethnic groups tested. In general these results substantiate previous research which found ethnicity to be a confounding variable on locus of control (49).

As a group, the White sample, in comparison with the Mexican-American sample, showed significant differences in locus of control. While the White sample tended toward internality, the Mexican-American sample showed high externality. There were also significant differences between the same groups with regard to self-concept assessment.

In contrast, the Mexican-American sample, in comparison with the Black sample, showed significant differences in both locus of control and self-concept assessment, e.g., Mexican-Americans reported more internality and favorable self-concepts.

Significant differences were found also between the White and the Black samples on both locus of control and self-concept, with the former group demonstrating more internality and more favorable on self-concept.

In this study the data with regard to ethnicity showed a hierarchical rating pattern for both locus of control and self-concept scores, with the Blacks and Mexican-American groups tending toward more externality and unfavorable self-concept evaluations than the White group. Furthermore, analysis of the demographic data gathered from the research questionnaire for the three groups indicated, on the average, that the Blacks and Mexican-Americans have spent more time in correctional facilities, including CRC, than their White peers. Previous research of the CRC residents by Levy noted that the Black and Mexican-American groups were somewhat older when admitted to the institution, spent more time there and were less successful parole risks than the White group.

There are a number of alternative explanations to account for the low scores on both locus of control (externality) and self-concept (negative ratings) by the Blacks in both the 1970 and 1990 studies. A recent national survey has indicated that staying in school is positively related to chemical abstinence by Black students.

According to the survey:

Black adolescents who stay in school have significantly lower alcohol and drug use than their White classmates, according to the survey conducted by Atlanta-based National Parents' Resource Institute for Drug Education, Inc. (PRIDE).

Statistics from a national survey of 350,000 students show the public has been misled about the extent of White versus Black drug abuse among teenage students.

Peter Bell, executive director of the Institute on Black Chemical Abuse in Minneapolis, hailed the PRIDE study. "What has now been substantiated, contrary to popular belief, is the fact that most Black youth do not have drug and alcohol abuse problems," Bell says.

Bell said the report "appropriately indicates the need for all of us to redouble our efforts in developing programs and services for those adolescents who are not in school or who lack supportive parents (50)."

In general, on the basis of the ethnic differences found here, future research should control for ethnicity as a possibly confounding variable.

Because both locus of control and self-concept investigations have demonstrated that socio-economic class affects these dimensions, this study determined the socio-economic status between both first and recidivist offenders and younger and older offenders. It is evident that the majority of both first and recidivist and younger and older residents (1970 and 1990) came from Warner's Class IV (Upper-Lower) and V (Lower-Lower) (51), and all CRC residents came preponderantly from a lower socio-economic strata. Because a homogeneity existed on social class evaluations, the writer assumed the differences found between the samples on locus of control and self-concept would not be attributable to divergent socio-economic identifications. These results demonstrate the need for even further investigation into self-concept and locus of control with drug users.

CHAPTER V.

REFERENCES

1. NATIONAL DRUG CONTROL STRATEGY. U.S. Government Printing Office, 1989, P. 18.

2. OFFICE OF STATE PRINTING, "Toward A State of Self-Esteem", *California State Department of Education*, copyright 1990, pp. 85, 86.

3. BENNETT, W. "How to Win the War on Drugs". *Fortune*, 3-12-90, P. 74.

4. NATIONAL INSTITUTE ON DRUG ABUSE, 1987.

5. NATIONAL INSTITUTE ON DRUG ABUSE, 1987.

6. NATIONAL INSTITUTE ON DRUG ABUSE, 1987.

7. RICHARD, W. C., MATES, C. G. and WHITTEN, L. "Personality traits and attitudes of adolescent girls with behavior disorders". Unpublished paper, presented at Southeastern Psychol. Associat., 1967.

8. LADWIG, G. W. "Personal, situational and social determinants of preference for delayed reinforcement". Unpublished doctoral dissertation, Ohio State University, 1963.

9. ROTTER, J. B. "Generalized expectancies for internal versus external control of reinforcement". Psychol. Monogr., 1966, 80, pp. 1-27.

10. SEEMAN, M. "Social learning theory and the theory of mass society". Unpublished paper presented at the American Social. Society, 1963.

11. SYKES, G. M. and MATZA, D. "Techniques of neutralization: a theory of delinquency". Amer. sociol. Rev., 1957, 22, pp. 664-670.

12. LARNER, J. and TEFFERTELLER, R. _The addict in the street._ New York: Grove Press, Inc., 1964.

13. LASKOWITZ, D. "Psychological characteristics of the adolescent addict". _In Harms, E._ (ed.). "Drug addiction in youth". _Oxford: Pergamon Press, 1965._

14. LINDESMITH, A. _Addiction and opiates._ Chicago: Aldine Publishing Company, 1968.

15. DORN, D. S. " Self-concept, alienation, and anxiety in a contraculture and subculture: a research report". _J. crim. law, crim. and pol. Science,_ 1968, 59, pp. 531-535.

16. KENNEDY, W. C. "Prisonization and self-conception: a study of a medium security prison". Unpublished doc-

toral dissertation, University of California, Los Angeles, 1970.

17. BALESTER, R. J. "The self concept and juvenile delinquency". Unpublished doctoral dissertation, Vanderbilt University, 1956.

18. LEFEBER, J. A. "The delinquent's self concept". Unpublished doctoral dissertation, University of Southern California, 1965.

19. AUSUBEL, D. P. *Drug Addiction: physiological,psychological and sociological aspects.* New York: Random House, Inc. 1965.

20. BORDIN, E. S. "Dimension of the counseling process". *J. Clin. Psychol.*, 1948, 4, pp 240-244.

21. PATTERSON, C. H. *Theories of counseling and psychotherapy.* New York: Harper and Row, Publishers, 1966.

22. GLASSER, W. *Reality Therapy.* New York: Harper and Row, Publishers, 1965.

23. CASRIEL, D. *So fair a house: the story of synanon.* New Jersey: Prentice-Hall, Inc. 1963.

24. ROGERS, C. R. *Client centered therapy.* **Cambridge: Riverside Press, 1951.**

25. TOLER, A. and REZNIKOFF, M. **"Relation between insight, repression-sensitization, internal-external control, and death anxiety".** *J. abnorm. Psychol.,* **1967, 72, pp. 426-430.**

26. WEINGARTEN, E. M. **"A study of selective perception in clinical judgment".** *J. Pers.,* **1949, 17, pp. 369-406.**

27. CASRIEL, D. *So fair a house: the story of synanon.* **New Jersey: Prentice-Hall, Inc. 1963. Publishers, 1965.**

28. GLASSER, W. *Reality Therapy.* **New York: Harper and Row, Publishers, 1965, P. XV.**

29. GLASSER, W. *Reality Therapy.* **New York: Harper and Row, Publishers, 1965, P. XV.**

30. GLASSER, W. *Reality Therapy.* **New York: Harper and Row, Publishers, 1965, P. 32.**

31. GARRITY, D. L. *The prison as a rehabilitation agency.* **In BERSANI, C. A. (ed.).** *Crime and delinquency.* **London: Collier-Macmillan Limited, 1970.**

32. DUSTER, T. *The legislation of morality.* **New York: The Free Press, 1970, P. 151.**

33. ROTTER, J. B. *Social learning and clinical psychology.* Englewood Cliffs: Prentice-Hall, 1954.

34. AUSUBEL, D. P. *Drug Addiction: physiological, psychological, and sociological aspects.* New York: Random House, Inc. 1965.

35. SCHIFF, S. "A self-theory investigation of drug addiction in relation to age of onset". Unpublished doctoral dissertation. New York University, 1959.

36. HURLEY, W. H. "A study of the self-concepts of criminals and non-criminals". Unpublished doctoral dissertation, The University of Oklahoma, 1961.

37. SCHIFF, S. "A self-theory investigation of drug addiction in relation to age of onset". Unpublished doctoral dissertation. New York University, 1959.

38. TAYLOR, D. M. "Changes in the self concept with psychotherapy". *J. consult. Psychol.,* 1955, 19, pp. 205-209.

39. RAIMEY, V. C. "The self-concept as a factor in counseling and personality". Unpublished doctoral dissertation, Ohio State University, 1948.

40. ROGERS, C. R. *Client centered therapy.* Cambridge: Riverside Press, 1951.

41. COLE, E. W., OETTING, E. R. and MISKIMINS, R. W. "Self-concept therapy for adolescent females". J. abnorm. Psychol., 1969, 74, pp. 642-645.

42. DUVALL, H. J., LOCK, B. Z. and BRILL, L. "Follow-up study of narcotic drug addicts five years after hospitalization". Public Health Rep., 1963, 78, pp.185-193.

43. FITTS, W. H. and HAMNER, W.T. "The self concept and delinquency; studies on the self concept and rehabilitation". Nashville mental health center Monogr., 1969, 1, pp. 1-96.

44. RICHARD, W. C., MATES, C. G. and WHITTEN, L. "Personality traits and attitudes of adolescent girls with behavior disorders". Unpublished paper, presented by Southeastern Psychol. Associat., 1967.

45. FREEDMAN, A. M. *The community mental health approach.* In STRAUS, N. *Addicts and drug abuses: current approaches to the problem.* New York: Twane Publishers, Inc., 1971.

46. AUSUBEL, D. P. *Drug Addiction: physiological, psychological, and sociological aspects.* New York: Random House, Inc. 1965.

47. WOOD, R. W. "The civil narcotics program: a five year progress report". *Lincoln law Rev.*, 1957, 2, pp.116-138.

48. DUSTER, T. *The legislation of morality.* New York: The Free Press, 1970.

49. LEFCOURT, H. M. and LADWIG, G. W. "The American Negro: a problem in expectancies". *J. pers. soc. Psychol.*, 1965, 1, pp. 377, 380.

50. *P.R.I.D.E.*, National Survey Shows Black Students Less Likely to Use Drugs Than White Students, 1989.

51. WARNER, W. L., MEEKER, M.L., and EELLS, K. W., *Social class in America.* New York: Harper Torchbooks, 1960.

CHAPTER VI

There is Still Work to be Done

RECOMMENDATIONS FOR FUTURE DRUG RESEARCH

Psychological investigators such as Freedman (1) and others have called for further exploration and research into the personality dynamics of drug users in order to formulate an explanatory typology of the drug user, particularly in terms of treatment outcome. As confirmed by this study, the positive relationship between locus of control and self-concept offers the potential for development of such typology. Furthermore, locus of control and self-concept are key factors pertinent for determination of which drug users should be initially accepted for treatment at CRC. The results of the writer's two studies demonstrate that further research is essential.

Several general comments can be made concerning the CRC sample used in these investigations. A first comment concerns the size of both the 1970 and 1990 CRC samples. It would have been ideal to use a larger and perhaps more representative sample of CRC drug users. Because the primary research instruments used were self-administered and brief, they provided an opportunity for enlargement of the research group. However, an essential reason for selection of the sample of 48 subjects stemmed from suggestions made by CRC staff to the effect that use of a larger group would tend to disrupt the institution's daily routine.

While it might prove difficult to obtain a matched sample of non-drug users it can be argued that comparative data from a control group would afford greater generalizability of the findings. Evidence from another self-concept study with juvenile delinquents indicated the value of using a control group (2).

A second comment concerning the CRC sample applies to the voluntariness of the subjects. While the writer purported that the samples, during both studies, 1970 and 1990, were voluntary; nevertheless, at the time of the testings, the CRC administration placed sufficient, subtle pressure on the residents to show up for testing sessions as to question the true voluntariness of the samples. It would have been desirable, from the writer's point of view, to randomly select the subjects independent of CRC intervention and future research there might want to do so.

Whether or not these subject sampling areas regarding size, absence of a control group, and voluntariness restricted the results of this study is uncertain; however, it would be wise for future research studies to guard against these potential sources of difficulty.

A third comment with regard to the research methodology can also be noted. Although this investigation was not concerned with measurement of the therapeutic processes at work at CRC, one might assume that whether or not an individual was actively involved in a particular treatment program would tend to affect both measures of locus of control and self-concept. It would have proven worthwhile, for example, to determine which residents were involved in particular therapy programs. While it is clear that the cross-sectional methodology used in this study had certain advantages, for future research it would be advisable to combine this method with a pre-post design to check for longitudinal changes.

A fourth area concerns the degree to which the findings from a number of prior locus of control and self-concept studies can be extrapolated to the present study. Several of these investigations used female subjects; therefore, it is unknown whether those specific results had meaning for the present study. With regard to sex differences on locus of control, Feather (3) has clearly demonstrated that there are locus of control differences between the sexes. He wrote: "The sex differences obtained in the present study strongly suggest that this variable should be taken into account in future research"(4). Thus, on Feather's recommendation, it would have been desirable to include only those studies conducted with male subjects. Moreover, it would be essential for future research at CRC to take notice of this suggestion.

A number of implications for future research with drug users at CRC accruing from this study are contingent upon the limits of the investigation. The writer suggests that future research at CRC or similar facilities should attempt to increase the sample size, include a non-drug using control group, insure absolute voluntariness of the subjects as well as socio-economic class control.

A number of self-concept investigations have indicated that the Osgood Semantic Differential Technique, the technique used to measure self-concept in the CRC studies, does lend itself to statistical quantification necessary to make it a highly acceptable self-concept scale (5). Yet the use of a more sophisticated self-concept scale that might enable a more detailed exploration of self-concept as well as promote comparison of these findings with other investigations is indicated.

The 1990 inclusion of the Carlson Personality Survey, CPS, is seen as an improvement. The CPS has had specific applications with prison inmates. Carlson (6) reports using the CPS with state prison inmates, federal inmates, female offenders and probationers. The CPS Self Depreciation Scale was used to tap the CRC sample's self-concept. The CPS Chemical Abuse Scale was also used with the 1990 sample.

The Cades Inventories (7) is reported to be increasingly utilized for evaluation of self-concept with a variety of deviant groups, including drug users. The use of the Cades Inventories would enable a more global self-concept appraisal, and promote cross-study comparison.

Since the appearance of Clemmer's (8) "universal factors of prisonization" a steady stream of institutional research has been generated to substantiate or refute his theoretical viewpoint that "these universal factors are sufficient to make a man characteristic of the penal community and probably so disrupt his personality that a happy adjustment in any community becomes impossible (9)." On the basis of prisonization theory a meaningful side issue for future research at CRC, or at a similar institution, could be centered around the effect of prisonization on locus of control and self-concept of institutionalized drug users. For instance, Kennedy (10) found evidence to support the view that highly prisonized offenders were significantly different on several personality measures from their less prisonized peers. Kennedy reported that the former group was more committed to the deviant subculture and showed less favorable self-concepts than the latter group. In keeping with these findings one could assume that a group of highly prisonized CRC residents would show externality and less favorable self-concept while a group of less prisonized residents might show the reverse.

It is additionally recommended that chemical dependency research should be directed toward explication of the effect if any that identification with an inmate power group might have on locus of control and self-concept. Clemmer (11) reported that the prisoners he studied were clearly divided into three aggregates. He labeled these the elite class, the middle class and the Hoosier class. This class or group division of power in the institution was believed to determine an inmate's range of roles, patterns of interaction, and relative status inside the institution. Grossner has also (12) pointed out that while affiliation with an inmate power group or elite clique tends to enhance an inmate's self-esteem, non-membership or rejection from such groups often serves to encourage hostility and attendant self deprecation.

Especially today, with the appearance of innumerable new and powerful inmate groups, e.g., Black Power, Brown Berets, etc., offering membership to chosen inmates, there is sufficient research opportunity to be able to assess the psychological differences between members and non-members. On the same note, locus of control studies have shown significant differences between social action takers and non-social action takers (13,14). These writers concluded that social action takers were more internal than the non-action takers. This is an

Drug Addicts: Are They Out of Control?

interesting and important point of view, and one which might carry over to a large institution like CRC which has a number of political power groups represented. On the premise that inmates affiliated with an inmate power group, like the Black Power, would be more internal and reflect a more favorable self-concept than non-members, future research should be designed to test for such differences.

Moreover, research of these power groups might also cast some light on the ethnic differences noted in this study. While the differences on locus of control and self-concept between the ethnic groups in this study are only suggestive, hopefully future research will specifically embrace this area.

Based on these research studies, it can be reasoned that older drug offenders who rely on external locus of control are not particularly suited for the treatment philosophy or the therapeutic methods available at CRC. In other words, while CRC might be effective with one type of drug offender, it might be equally ineffective with another. Therefore, it logically follows that a number of CRC residents who violate the conditions of parole on release should not have been sent to CRC for treatment. In general, these results substantiate previous research which found ethnicity to be a confounding variable on locus of control.

Previous research of the CRC residents by Levy (15) noted that the Black and Mexican-American groups were somewhat older when admitted to the institution, spent more time there and were less successful parole risks than the White group. These factors may also help explain why the Blacks and Mexican-American groups were more external on locus of control measures. It may also be the case that because these two groups spent more time in correctional settings, including drug treatment facilities, that they had become more institutionalized and more external.

In this study the data with regard to ethnicity showed a hierarchical rating pattern for locus of control scores, with the Blacks and Mexican-American groups tending toward externality evaluations when compared with the White group. This research finding proved true for both the 1970 and 1990 samples. Furthermore, analysis of the demographic data gathered from the research questionnaire for the three groups indicated, on the average, that the Blacks and Mexican-Americans have spent more time in correctional facilities, including CRC, than their White peers. This fact may help explain their higher external ratings. These results are in agreement with the earlier work conducted by Lefcourt and Ladwig(16). They found that Black prison inmates were external on locus of control measures compared with White prisoners.

In addition to research to better understand drug use and ethnicity, we must also address the issue of drug education, perhaps the first line of defense against chemical dependency. The information concerning the widespread drug use and sales of narcotics at American schools is truly alarming. For example, a 1989 Gallup report demonstrates that both use and sales of drugs are increasing (17).

The CRC drug treatment model does involve the use of a drug educational policy which may help explain that institution's positive impact on recidivism. The complete CRC educational program is detailed in Chapter II. Research suggests that educational programs, combined with a treatment modality, is essential for the rehabilitation of the drug user.

Finally, the results of the present study, which is the first one known to report a positive relationship between locus of control and self-concept among drug users has certainly added to our theoretical understanding of the personality dynamics of the drug user. It is recommended that future research further analyze these two personality dimensions, in combination with other characteristics, to develop a more explanatory typology of the drug user.

CHAPTER VI

REFERENCES

1. FREEDMAN, A.M. *The community mental health approach.* In STRAUS, N. *Addicts and drug abuses: current approaches to the problem.* New York: Twane Publishers, Inc., 1971.

2. DIETZ, G. E. "A comparison of delinquents with non-delinquents on self-concept, self-acceptance, and parental identification". *J. genet. Psychol.*, 1959, 115, pp. 285-295.

3. FEATHER, N. T. "Some personality correlates of external control". Australian J. Psychol., 1967, 19, pp. 253-260.

4. FEATHER, N. T. "Some personality correlates of external control". Australian J. Psychol., 1967, pp. 19, 257

5. OSGOOD, C. E., SUCI, G. J. and TENNENBAUM, P. H. "The measurement of meaning". Urbana: Univ. of Illinois Press, 1957.

6. CARLSON, K. *Psychological Survey, Research Psychologists Press, Inc.* London Ontario, 1982.

7. CADE, A. J. "The relationship between counselor-client cultural background similarity and counseling

progress". Unpublished doctoral dissertation. Michigan State University, 1963.

8. CLEMMER, D. "The prison community (new edition)". New York: Rinehart, 1958. P. 300.

9. CLEMMER, D. "The prison community (new edition)". New York: Rinehart, 1958. P. 300.

10. KENNEDY, W. C. "Prisonization and self conception: a study of a medium security prison". Unpublished doctoral dissertation, University of California, Los Angeles, 1970.

11. CLEMMER, D. "The prison community (new edition)". New York: Rinehart, 1958.

12. GROSSNER, G. H. *External setting and internal relations of the prison.* In Hazelbrigg, L. (ed.). Prison within *society.* New York: Doubleday and Company, Inc., 1969.

13. GORE, P. M. and Rotter, J. B. "A personality correlate of social action". *J. Pers., 1963,* 31, pp. 58-64.

14. STRICKLAND, B. "The prediction of social action from a dimension of internal-external control". *J. soc. Psychol.,* 1965, 66, pp. 353-358.

15. LEVY, M. "Study of the differences between Mexican-American, Caucasian, and Negro institutionalized drug addicts and the relationship between these differences and success on parole". Unpublished paper presented at Western Psychol. Associat., 1967.

16. LEFCOURT, H.M. and LADWIG, G.W. "The American Negro: a problem in expectancies". *J. Pers. Soc. Psychol,* *1965,* 1, pp. 377, 380.

17. GALLUP, G.H. *George Gallup International Foundation,* August 1980.

APPENDIX I

LIFE CONTROL QUESTIONNAIRE INSTRUCTIONS

This is a questionnaire to find out the way in which certain important events in our society affect different people. Each item consists of a pair of choices lettered a or b. Please select the one statement of each pair (and only one) which you more strongly believe to be the case as far as you're concerned. Be sure to select the one you actually believe to be more true and not the one you think you should choose as the one you would like to be true. On this type of questionnaire obviously there are no right or wrong answers. You can score your own questionnaire by using the instructions at the end of the scale.

1. a. Children get into trouble because their parents punish them too much.

   b. The trouble with most children nowadays is that their parents are too easy with them.

2. a. Many of the unhappy things in people's lives are partly due to bad luck.

   b. People's misfortunes result from the mistakes they make.

3. a. One of the major reasons why we have wars is because people don't take enough interest in politics.

   b. There will always be wars, no matter how hard people try to prevent them.

4. a. In the long run people get the respect they deserve in this world.

   b. Unfortunately, an individual's worth often passes unrecognized no matter how hard he tries.

5. a. The idea that teachers are unfair to students is nonsense.

   b. Most students don't realize the extent to which their grades are influenced by accidental happenings.

6. a. Without the right breaks one cannot be an effective leader.

   b. Capable people who fail to become leaders have not taken advantage of their opportunities.

7. a. No matter how hard you try some people just don't like you.

   b. People who can't get others to like them don't understand how to get along with others.

8. a. Heredity plays the major role in determining one's personality.

    b. It is one's experiences in life which determine what they're like.

9. a. I have often found that what is going to happen will happen.

    b. Trusting to fate has never turned out as well for me as making a decision to take a definite course of action.

10. a. In the case of the well prepared student there is rarely if ever such a thing as an unfair test.

    b. Many times exam questions tend to be so unrelated to course work that studying is really useless.

11. a. Becoming a success is a matter of hard work; luck has little or nothing to do with it.

    b. Getting a good job depends mainly on being in the right place at the right time.

12. a. The average citizen can have an influence in government decisions.

    b. This world is run by the few people in power and there is not much the little guy can do about it.

13. a. When I make plans, I am almost certain that I can make them work.

    b. It is not always wise to plan too far ahead because many things turn out to be a matter of good or bad fortune anyhow.

14. a. There are certain people who are just no good.

b. There is some good in everybody.

15. a. In my case getting what I want has little or nothing to do with luck.

b. Many times we might just as well decide what to do by flipping a coin.

16. a. Who gets to be the boss often depends on who was lucky enough to be in the right place first.

b. Getting people to do the right thing depends upon ability; luck has little or nothing to do with it.

17. a. As far as world affairs are concerned, most of us are the victims of forces we can neither understand nor control.

b. By taking an active part in political and social affairs the people can control world events.

18. a. Most people don't realize the extent to which their lives are controlled by accidental happenings.

b. There really is no such thing as "luck."

19. a. One should always be willing to admit mistakes.

b. It is usually best to cover up one's mistakes.

20. a. It is hard to know whether or not a person really likes you.

b. How many friends you have depends upon how nice a person you are.

21. a. In the long run the bad things that happen to us are balanced by the good ones.

    b. Most misfortunes are the result of lack of ability, ignorance, laziness, or all three.

22. a. With enough effort we can wipe out political corruption.

    b. It is difficult for people to have much control over the things politicians do in office.

23. a. Sometimes I can't understand how teachers arrive at the grades they give.

    b. There is a direct connection between how hard I study and the grades I get.

24. a. A good leader expects people to decide for themselves what they should do.

    b. A good leader makes it clear to everybody what their jobs are.

25. a. Many times I feel that I have little influence over the things that happen to me.

    b. It is impossible for me to believe that chance or luck plays an important role in my life.

26. a. People are lonely because they don't try to be friendly.

    b. There's not much use in trying too hard to please people, if they like you, they like you.

27. a. There is too much emphasis on athletics in high school.

b. Team sports are an excellent way to build character.

28. a. What happens to me is my own doing.

b. Sometimes I feel that I don't have much control over the direction my life is taking.

29. a. Most of the time I can't understand why politicians behave the way they do.

b. In the long run the people are responsible for bad government on a national as well as on a local level.

Now that you have completed this assessment, use the following scoring to check your Life Control Center.

LOCUS OF CONTROL SCORING

Score for Externality

2.A	9.A	16.A	23.A
3.B	10.B	17.A	25.A
4.B	11.B	18.A	26.A
5.A	12.B	20.A	28.A
6.A	13.B	21.A	29.A
7.A	15.B	22.B	

If your score is:			
2 - 5	6 - 0	10 - 16	16 - 23
High Internal	Mild Internal	Mild External	High External
This means you are:			
In Control	Mostly In Control	Fate Plays A Small Role	Generally Chance, Fate, and Luck Runs Your Life

APPENDIX II

SELF CONCEPT SCALE

Instructions

We would like to enlist your cooperation as a participant in a study designed to evaluate certain features of Corona. The purpose of this study is to measure the meaning of certain things to various people like the Corona residents by having them judge them against a series of 25 adjective-description scales. The task simply involves judging the following concept against these descriptive adjective pairs. The concept to be rated is: "ME AS I REALLY AM." This questionnaire should take you no more than 5 or so minutes to fill out.

It is your first impressions, the immediate "feelings" about the items that we want. But, of course, do not be careless on the ratings. Please go ahead and complete all 9 ratings even though it may be difficult or seem to you that you "just don't have the information."

All test results will be held strictly confidential as is customary and is our ethical responsibility in investigations of this nature.

Here is how to use the scales:

If you feel that the concept I or concept II is very closely related to one end of the scale, you should place your check mark as follows:

Good	X						Bad

If you feel that it is quite close but not extremely close to one or the other end of the scale you should place your check mark as follows:

Sucessful			X			Failure

If you consider that the concept is neutral on the adjective scale, both sides of the scale equally associate with the concept, or if the scale is completely irrelevant you should place your check mark in the middle space.

Unusual			X			Average

Please Rate: "Me as I really am."

Valuable							Worthless
Clean							Dirty
Tasty							Distasteful
Fast							Slow
Active							Passive
Hot							Cold
Large							Small
Strong							Weak
Deep							Shallow

APPENDIX III

WARNER SCALES FOR MAKING PRIMARY RATINGS OF FOUR STATUS CHARACTERISTICS

Status Characteristics and Rating	Definition

Occupation: Original Scale

1. Professionals and Proprietors of large businesses

2. Semiprofessionals and smaller officials of large businesses

3. Clerks and kindred workers

4. Skilled workers

5. Proprietors of small businesses

6. Semiskilled workers

7. Unskilled workers

Source of Income:

1. **Inherited wealth**

2. **Earned wealth**

3. **Profits and fees**

4. **Salary**

5. **Wages**

6. **Private relief**

7. **Public relief and nonrespectable income**

House Type: Original Scale

1. Large houses in good condition

2. Large houses in medium condition; medium-sized house in good condition

3. Large houses in bad condition

4. Medium-sized houses in medium condition; apartments in regular apartment buildings.

5. Small houses in good condition; small houses in medium condition; dwellings over stores

6. Medium-sized houses in bad condition; small houses in bad condition

7. All houses in very bad condition; dwellings in structures not intended originally for homes.

House Type: Revised Scale

1. Excellent houses

2. Very good houses

3. Good houses

4. Average houses

5. Fair houses

6. Poor houses

7. Very poor houses

Dwelling Area:

1. Very high: Gold Coast, North Shore, etc.

2. High: the better suburbs and apartment house areas, houses with spacious yards, etc.

3. Above average: areas all residential, larger than average; areas all residential, larger than average space around houses; apartment areas in good condition, etc.

4. Average: residential neighborhoods, no deterioration in the area.

5. Below average: areas not quite holding their own, beginning to deteriorate, business entering, etc.

6. Low: considerably deteriorated, run down and semi-slum

7. Very low: slum

Status Characteristic	Weight	Factor Missing				Directions
Occupation	4	5	-	5	5	Rate each char-acteristic fron 1 to 7; multiply by weight; total will fall be-tween 12 and 84
Source of Income	3	-	5	4	4	
House Type	3	4	4	-	3	
Area Lived In	2	3	3	3	-	

SOCIAL CLASS EQUIVALENTS		
12-32 Upper	38-51 Lower-Middle	68-84 Lower-Lower
23-37 Upper-Middle	52-66 Upper-Lower	

ORDER FORM

Psychology Systems, Inc.
615 South Main Street
Milpitas, CA 95035
(408) 263-8046
(800) 992-8448

Additional copies of DRUG ADDICTS: ARE THEY OUT OF CONTROL?, as well as the following studies, may be obtained by completing the order form below.

Please send me the following:

# of copies

_____	Drug Addicts: Are They Out of Control? (Hardback $17.00)	$ _____
_____	Drug Addicts: Are They Out of Control? (Paperback $10.00)	$ _____
_____	Big Bucks in Drug Abuse Clinics ($2.00)	$ _____
_____	The High Price of Mental Health ($2.00)	$ _____
_____	Substance Abuse and Treatment ($2.00)	$ _____
		Total$ _____

Price Includes Sales Tax and Shipping

Pease Rush To:

Name _____

Address _____

City _____ **State** _____ **Zip** _____